CINDERFELLAS
WHEN SPEEDWAY WAS ROCK 'N' ROLL

DAVE LANNING

Book Guild Publishing
Sussex, England

Published in Great Britain in 2013 by
The Book Guild Ltd
Pavilion View
19 New Road
Brighton, BN1 1UF

First published in 2011 by Centenar Publishing
Copyright © Dave Lanning 2011, 2013

Typesetting and design by Crispin Goodall

Printed and bound in Great Britain by
CPI Group (UK) Ltd, Croydon, CR0 4YY

A catalogue record for this book is available from
The British Library.

ISBN 978 1 84624 816 0

"The new England... of arterial and by-pass roads, of filling stations and factories that look like exhibition buildings, of giant cinemas and dance halls and cafes, bungalows with tiny garages, cocktail bars, Woolworths, motor coaches, wireless, hiking, factory girls looking like actresses, greyhound racing and dirt tracks."

J.B. Priestley, *An English Journey*

ACKNOWLEDGEMENTS

With sincere thanks for the help, support and inspiration from:

Warren Breach
Mike Mansfield
Tom Hickman
Tony Smith
John Chaplin
Crispin Goodall
Jason Crump
Leona Lanning

CHAPTER I

ADOLF HITLER drove triumphantly into Vienna on March 14, 1938, the same day as Jon 'Jacko' Rintzen arrived unnoticed on the dank, grey dockside of Tilbury, England.

He still wore the rough clothing of the Australian jackaroo, the origin of the nickname he'd known for as long as he could remember. Nobody had ever called him Jon. At first, he had just been 'Boy'.

When he joined the drovers, aged ten, he became 'Young Jacko'. As he swiftly developed into the most skilful and hard-riding of all the hands, the 'Young' had disappeared. In his teens, he became accepted as one hell of a worker on the Kerslake cattle station, which sprawled thousands of hectares across the Queensland/Northern Territory border, out into the fringes of the pitiless Simpson Desert, where from time to time man and beast died alone and desperate.

But the parched, blazing outback at the end of a six-week drought seemed more attractive to Jacko than the sight of a grim, March morning on Essex docks.

He only had the clothes he stood in, three pounds, two shilling and ninepence in English coinage, and a four-year-old, 497 cc., 27 bhp JAP speedway racing machine which did not actually belong to him, with two spare tyres, a raggedy set of racing leathers and a broad-peaked crash helmet. These were still stowed somewhere near the bilges of the bucket of a tramp freighter on which he had scrounged a passage nearly four months previously.

The few quid he had put by didn't cover his passage let alone that of the bike, so he had been forced to work his passage. He had shovelled and heaved coal, cleaned out the galleys and the heads, pumped the bilges and had been treated with roughly the same respect as the stinking Lascar seamen alongside whom he had slept in piles of sacking on the decks. He still wasn't exactly smelling like a watermelon vine having only been allowed to wash in leftover dishwater.

He had been topside only half a dozen times during the voyage to sniff the air for about five minutes before some mean-eyed nautical type had found a job for him.

It had not been a pleasure cruise for Jacko on his first experience, indeed first sight, of the ocean. Purgatory would have been preferable to Jacko, whose entire life had been in the wide open spaces, than being almost entombed in the bowels of the clanky old rust bucket, choked with the stink of marine oil and sweaty stokers.

Yet Jacko fretted not at all. He was used to rough living. He had always slept on the floor of the bunkhouse or out on the range. The most Spartan of monastic orders had not existed as frugally as Jacko.

He'd never known any different life. So he had never snivelled. But now, surveying the damp cobbles, rotting cranes and dripping outbuildings of the dreary docks, he felt elation, hope, optimism about the future.

He'd only bloody made it.

This was England, the land of amazing opportunity, where a bloke could make a quick fortune, where a bloke with a bit of go could find overnight fame on cinders of booming oval track speedway, in arenas that looked like something out of Roman history, with mystical names like Wembley, Belle Vue (Manchester), Harringay and West Ham.

That's what all the big-time talkers in the pits at Baranga Park and Eldura had said.

There had been blokes there that had spent a year in British speedway and earned enough to buy their own cattle station.

Hadn't he heard about Frank Arthur, Vic Huxley, Cyclone Billy Lamont, Max Grosskreutz and Ron Johnson who had helped introduce dirt track racing in Britain in 1928? Or a cove called Van Praag who had won the world title a couple of years back and around five hundred pounds in one night?

It was an existence almost beyond imagination for Jacko. He had, too, his own deep, painful reasons for starting out anew, to help wipe out memories which haunted him daily.

So, in England at last, the Promised Land. Jacko was ready to march in triumphantly. He had only a vaguest idea about this Hitler bloke who was doing similarly in Vienna.

FOR THE FIRST nineteen years of his life, Jacko had seen and knew about as much of the world as a stringy, long-horned steer. He had been born on the cattle station during a bitch of a twister. His first squawks inhaled half a lungful of red dust.

He had never known his mum. She had apparently been a good-timer with a voice like a parakeet whom his old dad had wooed and screwed while still wildly celebrating his survival from World War One. At the first opportunity to escape the iron existence at the cattle station she had disappeared forever, lured by the bright lights and gutters of the big city.

Everyone called his dad 'Rinz'. His past life was hazy. Even he hadn't been too sure of his family background. He was just another of a lost legion of nomadic Aussie immigrants, who had somehow eked out a life and avoided starvation in the outback during the early years of the twentieth century.

There had been hundreds like Rinz; loners, wanderers, rootless, accomplished horsemen, leathery, hard as nails, uncommunicative, sardonic, crude-humoured, with an odd, herd-like tendency to bond with identical male specimens.

They were drovers, they were rovers.

There was no place for women in the torturously tight masculine world of men like Rinz. He'd never considered marrying Jacko's mother. And she had disappeared from her son's life before he'd even recognised her smell.

Jacko had never felt at ease in the company of females. He had never had much chance to get to know any.

His dad hadn't exactly abandoned him, just palmed him out for unofficial adoption to the rest of the Kerslake cattle station. He scrounged food with the hands at meal calls, slept on the boards in the bunkhouse, sometimes dared to sneak into an empty bed when the hands were out on a drove, and somehow justified his keep by cheerfully tackling any chore or rotten job.

Jacko's dad had passed down traces of his mysterious lineage to his son. There was a discernible Northern European touch; a Teutonic thread maybe. Jacko had a thatch of yellow hair, with the appearance and texture of straw. It sprouted in all directions and refused to lie flat and tidy even when doused in tap water. He also had surprisingly bright, green-flecked eyes, again hinting at Nordic ancestry.

Like all cattle station folk, Jacko's eyes were mostly screwed up, squinting against the sun into the middle distance. But on occasions when he looked up or directly ahead, they were amazingly feline. Almost feminine. And very un-Aussie outback.

He'd also inherited his dad's scrawny, wiry body and his longish arms (Rinz had spent many years as a sheepshearer and cane cutter), as well as his big, useful hands and whiplash wrists, long fingers and very strong thumbs.

His teacher in the one-class outback school – an evil old biddy who repeatedly whacked Jacko on his bare legs when his attention regularly drifted out of the open window to the activity in the corral – said he looked a bit like somebody she called Huckleberry Finn.

The two little girls in the class giggled about that and poked fun at his bare feet.

Jacko learned to read and write but that was about it with education. Because, from the moment he first sat up and observed the world around him, Jacko had discovered his reason for living.

He was born to be with animals. He had his own world of wonderment with the abounding wildlife around him. He had a way with them; they came to him, responded to him, nuzzled, licked, rolled over, seemed to nod in agreement when he whispered to them. There did not appear to be one of God's beasts who didn't love Jacko Rintzen. The shyest wombat, even wandering, disagreeable camels, loved Jacko.

The unromantic blokes on the station reckoned he was born to be a horse doctor.

Occasional nomadic gaggles of old Aboriginals who drifted across the station shook their heads solemnly and muttered about magic. Jacko got on with the Abbos, although he thought it curious they didn't seem to have any kids.

But Jacko, the orphan of the outback, abandoned by a mother he never knew, virtually disowned by a dissolute father, existing on the flint-hard charity of a dusty cattle station, was still a happy kid. Because every animal was his pal. It was a curiosity, or maybe inevitability, that this tender, absolute passion of a lonesome lad in the heart of a mighty continent should one day project him into the razzmatazz circus of international speedway racing.

And impossible stardom.

CHAPTER 2

RINZ DIED more dramatically than he had lived. He had been rushed south with the more durable hands to assist fighting bastard bush-fires interstate.

He and his horse had been trapped by a sudden wind switch and burnt to a cinder.

Jacko cried big tears. He had thought the world of his dad's sturdy mount and thought it was a rotten way for a horse to die.

The awful truth that he was completely alone without a blood relative left in the world simply did not occur to Jacko. He had never called Rinz Dad. The bunkhouse was the only home he knew, the other hands and jackaroos his only family. Tough but uncomplicated outback life would simply continue as he knew it.

Still years short of his first shave, he was summoned to the presence of Kerslake, the cattle station owner, for the first time in his life.

Kerslake was a thickset, taciturn character who communicated mainly in terse grunts, was rarely seen without a shapeless slouch hat and indulged in sacrosanct sessions of solo beer drinking every sunset. He had never been known to show the slightest desire for female company.

"Hear you're useful with horses, boy," he sniffed. "Reckon you'll need knocking into shape as a drover.

"You'll have to earn your bloody keep now."

11

Jacko did not return to school lessons. Nobody seemed to care. He certainly did not. Horses were preferable company to tetchy school marms and soppy, smirking girls.

Cattle baron Kerslake proved a merciless task master.

Jacko was hoisted on horses bareback every day. He was not permitted a saddle. Kerslake insisted he used rough reins as little as possible. "Balance naturally, boy. Move with the mount. Go with him, learn to read his mind. When you can stay aboard all day like that, reckon you'll do."

Kerslake had been outraged by being forced into an involvement in the First World War by the Australian Government requisitioning his stock for meat and finest horses for the military. This equally fired a hatred of the Germans and their Kaiser for starting all the trouble and interrupting his driving ambition to build the most impressive cattle station in the territory. The Great War had set back the growth of his stock empire years. He retained a hornet in his slouch hat about it right up to the death of Wilhelm II in 1941.

"Bloody Kaiser Bill," he growled for over twenty years. "Upsetting folk twelve thousand miles from his own yard."

Scanning newsheets about the war as he swilled sundowners on the verandah, Kerslake learned about the Kaiser's deformed, virtually useless arm and how he had been ruthlessly trained as a boy to handle a horse despite his debility. Kerslake found perverse pleasure in reading that the monarch who had so disrupted his life and business had fallen frequently, been beaten, bruised and regularly driven to tears of frustration until he learned to ride reasonably efficiently for ceremonial occasions.

"If he could ride with one hand, boy, you'll learn to ride without using one at all," he said to Jacko. "An Aussie kid is better than any crippled Kraut Kaiser."

Immersed in awe and respect for the fearsome Kerslake, Jacko virtually became a horseback circus act. He fell regularly, but learned to bounce, roll, break the impact. He was trampled, kicked, scraped, abrased angrily as he was dragged or deposited in the dirt. Sand seemed to be permanently ingrained under his skin. He was never scabless.

But unlike the boy Kaiser he never shed a tear. Not in front of Kerslake, anyway. Weeks of training went into months. At nights when, exhausted, Jacko bedded down in the straw with the horses -- quite literally hitting the hay – he felt there was not a square inch of his body which did not ache, throb or tingle.

But nothing diminished his affection for horses. He was becoming quite a rider. The other hands, in off duty moments, observed his rigid training and unusual expertise, grudgingly approving. They thought Kerslake was trying to kill the boy.

Watching Jacko galloping around the corral like a performer in Buffalo Bill's Wild West Show, even Kerslake relented and snorted: "You're getting there, boy.

"Time you had a mount of your own."

BOWZ was hardly a show pony. Squat, a dirty, undistinguished roan with incredibly bandy back legs which had been the cause of his name, he was not popular with the hands, displaying distinctly mulish tendencies time and again. Equine nobility was not in his bloodline.

Yet he reacted like a thoroughbred to Jacko's touch. He seemed to relish a bareback rider. "Never did like a saddle, that bludger," said Head Hand Chazza, a surly sod. "An absolute bastard to break, a kick like a jackass if he doesn't like you."

A bastard to most, a beauty to Jacko.

Bowz seemed to recognise Jacko had an almost supernatural gift in horse handling. The boy became as one with his mount, he reacted in anticipation rather than reaction to every gallop, canter, trot, direction change. Bowz seemed to know he had someone very special aboard. All his quirkiness, skittishness disappeared when Jacko was around. It was love and mutual respect.

Jacko slipped out of the bunkhouse most nights to doss down with Bowz as he stretched in the straw. "Jeez, that daft boy uses old Bowz' croup as a pillow," said one hand. But the Jacko/Bowz partnership was accepted and welcomed into the workforce. Jacko willingly covered more ground than any of the more experienced drovers. Night watch was not a drag for him. Jacko and Bowz hunkered down together until each spectacular outback sunrise.

The two inseparables became a threesome when a bedraggled mixbreed hound limped into the bunkhouse yard. He was little more than a pup, more than half-starved, gasping for water, caked with desert red dust.

"Shoo that mongrel out of the yard," shouted Chazza.

"He'll die in that desert sun in a couple of hours," said another hand. "Kinder to put a quick bullet in his ear."

The dog lolloped drunkenly straight to Jacko, looked up agonisingly at him, tried to find his hand with a parched tongue.

"Hang on, I'll fetch you a drink, mate," said Jacko, another chunk of his heart melting.

"You'll never get rid of the mongrel now," snarled Chazza, as the dog slurped half a bucketful of water. "Go fetch the shotgun, Barney."

"No, please, please, I'll look after him. He'll be no trouble," pleaded Jacko.

"We can't feed a ratbag like him. Go get the gun…"

"He can have my food," said Jacko, appalled at the thought of a bullet and the

13

sprawled corpse of this friendly fellow.

It was Kerslake who intervened for Jacko.

"The boy has little enough in this world," he said. "If he's prepared to share his tucker with the mutt, let him keep it."

Jacko named him Blue. He clearly had Queensland Blue in his mix as Jacko discovered when he scrubbed off all the caked dirt and observed the natural greyish-blue hue of his shorthaired hide. The dog swiftly thrived and grew under Jacko's care and followed him everywhere. His outsized head became comically out of proportion to his body with jaws which developed like a beartrap. His testicles looked like swinging tennis balls; innocent prepubescent Jacko could not understand why the hands were so impressed by them. "The bastard's got courtin' bollocks," they said. Jacko did not understand the fuss.

Blue never left Jacko's heels, nor Bowz' hooves. He bonded famously with the horse. They shared the same water bucket. Blue loped alongside tirelessly as the team chased and chivvied longhorns over miles of unforgiving terrain. Now Jacko used Blue's muscular back as a pillow as they camped under the dazzling stars of the Southern Hemisphere, while Bowz seemed content to stand guard over the pair.

But Blue proved that although of dubious pedigree he was no hairy halfwit when Jacko drifted into potential disaster when caught out by treacherous outback weather conditions.

Moving equably, happily into his teenage years, Jacko, Bowz and Blue built up a reputation among the hands as maverick chasers. With Kerslake stock running into tens of thousands spread over mindboggling miles of outback, it was inevitable isolated pockets of steers and heifers would wander off to become detached from the main herds. Some would meander ten miles into empty country.

Usually, small groups would be abandoned, left to fend for themselves. Kerslake did not care much to have experienced drovers leaving the main herds for perhaps a couple of days rounding up a few dozy mavericks.

Unemotional oldtime drovers reckoned the critters could look after themselves, even in the outback. Bunkhouse scuttlebutt insisted disillusioned pioneer settlers one hundred and fifty years earlier had abandoned their herds to wander off. They had thrived and multiplied. Railroad companies had imported camels and turned them loose into the outback once the work was complete. Now they swore there were more camels in Australia than in the Sahara.

But Jacko knew camels were desert animals, natural survivors. Cattle, particularly young ones, struggled to survive. During his time as a drover – and he was experienced considerably beyond his teenage years – he had repeatedly stumbled across the grim

14

sight of the bleached bones of strays, mostly little ones, who had perished and been picked clean by predators and Australia's one hundred thousand-plus species of insect life. Jacko detested the thought of any animal suffering that fate.

So he frequently slipped away with Bowz and Blue to round up as many strays as possible.

They were tracking half a dozen heifers, last reported ambling towards a harsh finger of desert scrub when a blinding sandstorm whirled up, borne on a blowtorch blast hotter than Hades.

Although as naïve as a choirboy in so many worldly ways, Jacko was an old hand in desert discipline. If you were caught by unexpected rough elements, do not try to beat them or outrun them. Camp down and try to survive until the trouble passes. And pray that it does. Bowz could hardly go on anyway. His eyes were virtually blinded by solid dust and he was breathing like a traction engine. Jacko could not see more than five yards ahead. He was a prisoner of nature at her most wickedly wanton worst.

Jacko knew he could survive for a few days. He had a reasonable supply of water. Outback folk knew instinctively to carry a surplus of water. Toddlers had water bottles stuffed down their diapers. He also had a compass. It had belonged to his Dad, Rinz, the only item he had left to Jacko. But with his limited schooling, Jacko was no expert in its usage.

In the past when he had drifted astray, Bowz had always seemed to know the right direction home. But now Bowz could hardly see, and Jacko knew he dare not waste drinking water washing the horse's eyes.

He did not panic. He knew the station hands would realise he was missing and, cursing him colourfully, would come looking. But they would have only a vague idea which direction he had taken. Or how far he had gone.

Grimly Jacko realised he was in genuine danger of becoming a victim of unforgiving outback conditions, like his Dad before him.

Eventually the storm blew out, leaving a landscape Jacko did not recognise. The rough trail had been buried deep in sand drifts. He furiously tried to calculate which way to go while Blue sniffed the air with his porthole nostrils as though he had caught a whiff of a butcher's apron.

Then the dog simply bounded off. "Bet the old beauty will smell his way home," thought Jacko. "He can travel faster than Bowz with me on his back over this country. Gotta trust him. Just stay put and believe he can lead a rescue party back to me and Bowz."

He settled down for the wait, disturbed only by a pack of sinister wild dogs who began circling disturbingly closely until scattered by Bowz with a volley of vicious donkey-kicks.

When hours later Blue, blowing hard and yowling for attention, galloped into the Kerslake Cattle Station yard, the hands had only just realised Jacko was overdue. The boy was such a loner, went for days talking only to his animals.

"Jeez, it's old Bulky Bollocks," said Chazza. "Looks like the bastard is trying to tell us something. He'd never leave Jacko's side unless things were crook."

With Blue inexhaustibly forging ahead, Chazza and another hand called Humpback eventually reached Jacko, curled up under Bowz, dozing peacefully. He still had enough water left to bathe the horse's clogged eyes. Jacko was pinned to the ground by a delighted Blue, his great, ugly tail flailing the air.

Incredibly, on the return journey Blue had stumbled on two stray heifers and shepherded them back too.

When the party trooped back into the cattle yard, Kerslake, angrier than anyone had seen in years, roared at Jacko: "You ever go on a fartarsed caper like that again, boy, and I'll take a bullwhip to you.

"Bloody good job your mutt isn't as dopey as he looks."

But their misadventure was quickly forgotten. Jacko, Bowz and Blue continued to track mavericks. They covered mile after mile of outback in demanding, stamina-sapping conditions, sleeping rough, often parched, but always together.

Eventually Bowz accepted being saddled, making long hours on the range more comfortable for Jacko. Kerslake surprisingly showed expertise in saddlery. For a big, heavy man, he was a beautifully balanced, deft horseman. There had not been a day in forty years he had not been in the saddle. Saddlery was his special love.

"Bowz won't take any old saddle," he explained to an enraptured Jacko, stunned by Kerslake's interest. "He probably feels like I do in a tight collar. I'll find him a racing-style job."

Kerslake, in stunted sentences, told Jacko most hands preferred a heavier saddle with a raised cantle ("back bit of the saddle," barked Kerslake when Jacko looked mystified) and a high pommel ("front bit, you ignorant little drongo. Makes 'em feel they're in an armchair"). Kerslake could converse with his senior hands on the various advantages of perplexities like running martingales, curb chains, snaffles, stirrup leathers and cheek straps. It was way above Jacko's head. But the cattle baron adapted a light, flattish saddle which Bowz accepted with only a whimsical whinney.

As long as Jacko was sitting on it.

The other station hands were dryly amused by Kerslake's brusque rapport with Jacko. "The old bastard talks more to you than anyone," they said. "He even seems to like your horse and dog."

Thus Bowz and Blue shared Jacko's early teenage years as he grew into a teak-tough, loose limbed, self reliant, independent but awkwardly innocent young man.

A totally happy one, though.

Jacko was lonely no more. He was doing exactly what he wanted to do. He had Bowz and Blue, the most loyal friends a boy could hope for. Life, surely, could hold nothing better.

The idyll could not last forever.

When it shattered, his life changed forever.

JACKO saw the first snake but not the second.

With a fractional twitch of the right rein, he veered Bowz out of range. But there must have been a nest, or a mating pair, because Jacko knew he was in dire strife as Bowz reared and screamed and collapsed, sending him sprawling in the scrub.

Blue, all bared teeth and rigid neck hair, erupted four-pawed to confront the first reptile. As the snake struck again, Blue's lightning reflexes and powerful thighs easily swayed him aside, out of range. Then he struck, his powerful jaws and huge teeth snapping the snake's back.

Turning to the second one, Blue was now waiting for the deadly strike, again dodged gracefully, and again killed swiftly.

When Jacko reached the scene, his heart stopped, ice reached every fraction of his being.

The two broken reptiles, still twitching in the dust, were desert death adders. Australia has the fourteen most venomous snakes on the planet and Jacko knew the death adder is one of the deadliest. The grizzled guys back at the station frequently grunted a death adder could kill the strongest horse in minutes.

That was clearly the fate for poor Bowz. And Jacko knew he could do nothing about it. Amid spasms and saliva, with his head in Jacko's arms, Bowz died, with Blue squatting howling forlornly at his side.

And Jacko howled with him.

Kerslake sent a party of hands, armed with long handled shovels, out with instructions to bury Bowz deep. He knew Jacko would be shattered at the thought of his dear pal being left to the ravages of the outback. They buried his saddle with him. Jacko didn't want to keep it

"Gonna have to teach you to shoot, boy," he said to Jacko. "There are dozens of bastard killers out there. Shouldn't risk it without a gun." But the thought of killing any living creature was abhorrent to Jacko.

It seemed things couldn't possibly have been more painful for Jacko. But less than a month later, his very soul was wrenched apart again when he awoke to discover dear, dear Blue, now so vital to him, had simply stopped breathing in the night.

Maybe Blue, missing Bowz as much as Jacko, died of a broken heart.

Jacko was seventeen years old but knew absolutely, totally, utterly, that his world would never be the same again. His grief was like a colony of fire-ants feasting on his intestines.

He buried lovely, loyal, lollopy Blue deep under a lone eucalyptus tree, his tears slopping into gritty topsoil.

And he made a vow.

He would never, ever again permit himself to become so completely attached and devoted then destroyed by any living creature. He would find something else to love. Something that would not break him apart.

He was not then to know it would be something with the power of forty-eight horses, guzzled gallons of wood alcohol to the mile and would captivate and enrich the pleasures of millions from Manchester to Melbourne and twenty-one London underground stations from Upminster to Chancery Lane.

He was about to discover speedway.

BETWEEN working droves, branding and servicing, Kerslake's hands squeezed odd hours of recreation at Baranga Showgrounds Trotting Racing Gala -- locally known as The Trots

They packed the still-mooching, disconsolate Jacko into the back of Kerslake's bone-shaking pickup and humped into what served as the township.

Jacko brightened at the sight of the charioteers, hauled at astounding speeds by the majestic, high stepping, immaculately groomed throughbreds. These gallopers had nobility.

His mind raced, conjecturing how they maintained the discipline that prevented their doing what came naturally: breaking into a gallop.

Old Bowz would have been heaving for his head.

Jacko knew he must stop thinking that way. He must shut his mind to Bowz. And Blue.

At the end of official racing, he loitered around the paddock, looking at the noble nags, ready to give a hand wiping down.

The noise that cut the evening hit him like a perfectly aimed left hook. It sounded like a cross between a motorised saw and an angry chorus of wounded lions, yet there was a rhythm, a beat, that was orchestral.

Somebody had started up a very special motorcycle.

Jacko moved towards the sound, discovered what appeared to be the chariot jockeys changed from their racing silks into black leathers and pudding-basin helmets, revving skeletal motorcycles with extravagant handlebars and monstrously wide rear wheels.

"What are those?" he asked an oily oik on the outskirts of the group.

"Dirt trackers, mate. Don'cha know it's all the go all over Aussie. There's a practice now the Trots are over."

Jacko then noticed the fumes. They were acrid, intoxicating, uniquely distinct.

"What do they run on, snake oil?" he asked.

"Not far out, mate. It's wood alcohol. They used to dump it but it makes these beauts sing and scream. Down-and-outs will drink it if you leave it around. Then they die.

"Oil's different too. They reckon it's vegetable based or summat like that. Burn 'em together and you get that stink.

"These aren't like any other bikes.

"Dirt-track racing is, just, well, dirt-track racing. It's not just about the fastest bikes. It's about the blokes who sit on 'em."

Jacko was mystified that the riders all walked with a limp. "Have they all got injured legs?" he asked.

"Nar, they wear a steel shoe over their left boot," came the reply. "That's the foot they trail or stick down on the corners. Without one, well, they'd really being going hotfoot."

Jacko felt his jaw sag as he gawped at the first practice lap.

The rider was unreal. He accelerated from standstill to maximum revs in five seconds and when he reached the first left-hand turn on the trotting track, found even more power and then bloody well went sideways without reducing speed.

His left leg trailed out in line with the rear wheel. The purest, most ridiculous balancing act the world must surely have ever witnessed. The rear wheel sprayed a black spume of trot track surface right around the grass banking beyond the perimeter fence. Down the next straight, flat out again.

Bloody amazing.

Then two, then three riders were on the track together, ducking and diving and changing direction and shouldering each other wickedly while still bloody well going sideways.

Jacko had believed absolutely there could be no more exhilarating sight in the world than a wild stallion in the sensational symmetry of full gallop with its mane streaming in the evening air.

But this dirt track speedway came pretty close.

And, he thought, although a dirt bike might break his neck, it would never break his heart.

JUST switching from one mounted ride to another, thought Jacko, six weeks into an eye-opening new life. From Bowz' special saddle to the rigid, narrow, bone-hard dirt track job.

The hard-bitten hangers-on around the paddock reckoned he wasn't far short of a natural on his newly discovered mount, his own iron horse.

He'd had no trouble getting his first riding experience. Old man Kerslake, wanting to find something to ease Jacko's misery over the loss of his animals, fixed it for him – the speedway organiser was a pal. Jacko had also been pretty lucky to have made his first close friend that did not have four legs.

James 'Bongo' Drumma was two years his senior and ached to be a star of the speedways. But just as, after a few tentative laps, Jacko had looked part of a bike, Bongo always looked to be fighting it.

He'd allowed Jacko to use his machinery. Bongo's dad owned the saddlery in town and was regarded as pretty flush. Bongo's equipment was in top condition.

Although blatantly and patently lacking natural ability aboard a bike, Bongo was an absolute whiz at knowing what made them work. He talked about mysteries like 5000 rpm, total loss oil and high compression ratio.

Jacko just rode them.

And learned quickly.

He learned that a dirt bike, unlike a horse which headed in straight lines, always seemed to want to go sideways.

His natural sense of weight distribution made it second nature to him to 'go with the bike', as the old timers said. He learned you moved forward going into corners, sat back down the straights, blipped the throttle and deftly twitched your backside going into the turns. He learned it was the right leg that took all the weight when cornering and it was critical to have the right footrest exactly positioned. The left leg just sort of dangled. Bongo loaned him his steel shoe. Having spent so much of his life in bare feet, Jacko felt lopsided, clumsy.

Jacko learned he could corner with his left leg hardly touching the track.

Broadsiding – that's what they called it – round the four left-handed turns injected Jacko with the greatest adrenalin rush he had known in his young life. It even exceeded the thrill of easing a stallion over a five-bar gate.

Bongo had studied much of the theory of dirt track racing and collected articles written by famous, successful speedway stars attempting to explain the mysteries of the sport.

He showed Jacko an explanation of a broadside written by a legendary American called Sprouts Elder, one of the very first superstars who was reported to have earned over £3500 in one summer of the Roaring Twenties.

Jacko devoured it avidly but was still left mystified.

Elder had written: "On reaching a point almost at the beginning of the bend after having taken the straight at full throttle the rider cuts off the engine power. Then as he enters the bend the machine is made to incline well over to the left, at the same time with both wheels dead in line with each other.

"This operation is extremely difficult, involving as it does an acute sense of equilibrium on the part of the rider as well as great physical strength in the arms and wrists.

"In this way with the handlebars held rigidly the machine is allowed to slide bodily across the track until instinct tells the rider that it is time to correct the slide before too much speed is lost. The operation is accomplished by a quick jerk of the steering wheel almost to the point of full lock, thus putting the machine into the correct position for negotiating the bend.

"At this moment the engine is allowed to cut in again a full throttle producing what is termed a power skid, the effect of which can be compared to the sensation of a man who, after running at full speed over springy turf suddenly strikes a patch of slippery clay and has more than to double his exertions to maintain even half his initial speed.

"The motor is now racing and the back wheel spinning, for the faster it spins the more even is the slide, the whole of the rear of the machine swings outwards, trying its hardest to get away from the rider. The practised hand always has the 'pull' under control until the curve is completed. Then with a sigh of relief he tears through the next straight knowing there are five seconds or so respite before the next spasm.

"A perfect broadside is a delight to watch and can be accomplished by any first class rider on a reliable track with apparently effortless ease."

Bongo Drumma had a much less complicated theory. "Keep going as fast as you can and just hang on," he advised.

Jacko had been driving Kerslake's pickups since he was fourteen. He had been shown the rudimentaries and never given a second thought about driving around the section of the cattle station which had the semblance of a worn track. He had never had to worry about negotiating traffic. It was an eight mile drive to what served as Kerslake's front gate. It was a post with a painted sign Kerslake nailed to it.

Switching to two wheels seemed as natural as taking a leak. With his own extraordinarily sensitive hands and wrists, sharpened by lifelong horsemanship, he discovered he had natural throttle and clutch touch.

The twist-grip throttle went from zero to flat-out, stop to shut, as they said, in less than a quarter of the circumference of the handlebars. You had only a fraction of that scope guiding a galloping stallion. The clutch, masterfully doctored by Bongo, had a vicious bite, like a salt water crocodile.

Synchronising the two and accelerating away from a standing start seemed second nature to Jacko. It was rather like matching spurs and reins reaction on horseback. He himself wasn't sure how he did but he always seemed to get it right.

His control was so precise that within weeks of his oval track baptism he was leaving the starting grid with his front wheel not actually in contact with the track surface.

When he first threw a leg over a dirt track bike, Jacko realised the contraption did not possess brakes. "If you wanna slow, knock off the throttle," said Bongo. "If you gotta stop, hit a slide and lay the bike down." It made sense to Jacko. If a horse braked quickly by sticking his front legs in the dirt, the bloke aboard went straight over his head and landed on his earhole. The hands called that a 'boner' because it usually meant a cracked collar bone. Jacko had seen drovers with a switchback of lumps on their shoulders where repeatedly broken clavicles had healed unevenly.

"Laying down" did not come with difficulty for him, either. He had been able to turn Bowz sideways, roll over and step off. After less than an hour of practice on a speedway machine, he was sliding to earth within three bikes' lengths after motoring at more than half throttle.

Pits observers at Baranga were unanimous that this slender jackaroo was more than a bit special. "An absolute natural," they agreed. "Haven't seen anyone as good at Baranga before." Most speedway activity in Australia was promoted in Sydney, Brisbane, down the eastern seaboard. The Baranga Trotting centre was very much an off the beaten track.

His new chum Bongo, recognising that Jacko possessed a natural gift he would

22

never acquire, cheerfully redirected his speedway ambitions to a support role.

He never questioned Jacko's use of his equipment.

He built up a bike for him and the pair marked out a a rough track on a parched backlot at Kerslake's cattle station where together they spent every spare moment roaring round and round and round. He paid for the dope (alcohol fuel) and oil and tyres and gave Jacko an old set of scruffy leathers and boots.

Their own private track, situated miles into flat desert, offered no shade nor respite from a fireball sun. At sunsets, the glare was blinding, hitting a rider straight in the eyes entering one corner. It was a similar problem at Baranga. Rather than resite the track, Bongo constructed broad, visor-like peaks for their crash helmets. Jacko's wide, distinctive peaked helmet was to become his recognisable trademark throughout his career.

Bossman Kerslake helped Jacko some more. "Just don't spook the livestock," he growled at the pair in an unusually talkative moment. He allowed them to use the ramshackle station pick-up to hump their bikes about.

Jacko seemed to have been born with an instinct for the right racing line. Hour after hour, he tried switching lines, taking the middle line, cutting back.

"You need to find where the drive is," said Bongo. "And get both wheels back in line as quick as you can when you straighten up out of the turns."

Initially, Jacko frequently overcooked his cornering several times due to youthful confidence and impetuosity. In racing parlance, he pulled full-lockers or tankslappers and sprawled, highsided or overslid into the dirt, but shrugged off each spill. It was nowhere near as far to fall as going ass-up from fifteen hands high. Jacko's electric reflexes curled him protectively and loosely.

"Jeez, you bounce like a joey," grunted Bongo. "You even fall pretty."

Jacko realised the debt he owed to his chum, and determined to start contributing towards expenses.

There was only one way: getting a ride in the racing programme at Baranga Showground and copping some prize money.

Bongo agreed he was ready.

The grizzled ex-rider with skin like a walnut who ran the show agreed to give him a go in one of the handicaps. These were races with five or six riders, starting from staggered positions graded from one hundred yards behind the starting gate, which was called scratch. "You'll start off scratch," he growled. "And for Chrissake don't fall off because the five lunatics starting behind will run you over and chop you into rubby dubby."

Jacko was all set.

His new love affair was ready to be consummated.

He was also ready for another unique thrill. Winning.

CHAPTER 3

BARBECUE and exhaust fumes wafted together pungently as Baranga Showground sizzled like the hottest griddle.

Jacko sniffed diffidently. He didn't care much for the stink of burning meat. Still a teenager but already he hated eating meat. In the outback, however, the only alternative was to go hungry: vegetarian cuisine and even the rich seafood of the coastal zone hadn't penetrated his narrow existence.

He secretly dreamed of one day existing without meat at all; eating something which did not offend his conscience.

Not that food was on his mind as he faced his official racing debut.

It was certainly a different crowd at the Showground than for the Trots.

In the baking afternoon sun, families sprawled up the grass banks of the arena. All the men seemed to be in sweat-stained bush hats, taking beer by the neck. There were a lot of girls in printed cotton frocks around the paddock.

The joint positively buzzed with energy and excitement.

And Jacko was in race one. Off scratch.

"Just get your head down and ass up," advised Bongo, who was not deemed worthy of a programmed ride but had tuned the bike selflessly. "Remember, you've got fifty yards on the next bloke."

The starting system was simple enough: what appeared to be a length of knicker elastic tied to a pole on the outside of the track, stretched across it and released by an official in shirt, shorts and bare feet.

Jacko's hairspring reflexes as he dropped the clutch gained him yards advantage up to the first turn, which he slightly overshot, corrected, straightened the wheels in line for the straight.

The engine positively purred.

Bongo, who had been schooled by the legendary Frank Arthur, had said: "Stick middle. Don't leave any obvious gaps, inside or out."

It was just like all those training laps out at the cattle station.

The turns and laps seemed to lick through although Jacko was aware of the howl of his rivals' motors in his ear as he levelled out from the last turn and saw the chequered flag.

The chasing pack had only got within ten yards of him.

He had won his first competitive race.

"You bloody beauty," grinned Bongo, as he swung back into the pits. "That's three quid, And ten bob a start."

Jacko was delighted when his win was announced over a crackly PA system as "a win for yer own local boy" – which attracted a surprising burst of applause.

"Not bad, son," grunted the grizzled bossman. "Go out again after the break. But I'm putting you back on the fifty-yard mark."

Righto, thought Jacko. Another three pounds ten just for having a hayride.

But this time there was a bloke in front and a surly-looking customer on his inside, who glowered at him as the start was called.

Again, his start was impressive and he got to the first turn half a length up.

But Old Surly just kept going, gave him an elbow and as Jacko twisted instinctively to maintain contact with the bike, a faceful of dirt from his opponent's rear wheel stuffed his breath back down his windpipe.

Jacko was still struggling to regain shape and composure on the next turn when the backmarker, a man with international know-how who had been an English headliner at somewhere called Clapton, went by him on the outside and disappeared so swiftly into the distance that for a second Jacko feared he'd dropped a chain.

This speedway was clearly no backyard barbie.

Jacko was given one more outing. This time he was on the inside of Old Surly and this time he kept going at the first turn. He shouldered him out of the way, became aware his rival was no longer in the race, and realised he couldn't finish last.

It was not until the very last corner that the international backmarker again swept imperiously by, seemingly with an extra gear.

A third place. The bloke he dumped on his backside with the first corner shouldering pushed his bike back to the pits and gave Jacko a wry, lopsided smile and a nod.

Jacko's first speedway earnings, paid out in cash by the boss from the cab of a dun-coloured pick-up, was five pounds ten shillings: four points from three starts. It was the most money Jacko had known in his young life. He kept two pounds ten and gave Bongo three – Bongo'd fronted up for the dope and oil.

That night Jacko stayed overnight with Bongo's family in their attractive, cream-painted clapboard house in a hushed cul-de-sac abutting Baranga main street.

For the first time he had his own bedroom with a double bed, which later in the night surprisingly acquired Bongo's kid sister Bel, who at fifteen was ripe and randy and who crept in, literally jumping on him. Jacko wasn't clear what was going on, found it a bit of a shock and was sure that Bel, like all the other girls, was laughing at him, just teasing. He was racked with guilt and mortified that he'd abused his host's hospitality.

But in the morning Bel, chubby and happy like all the Drumma family, hadn't looked twice at him.

It was his first experience of the mysterious mind of the female.

JACKO became a regular on the programme at the Showground and just as naturally Bongo forgot his racing ambitions and settled down as a spannerman.

He won races, took a few horrendous tumbles but always bounced, sometimes took a spreadeagler at the turn but dished it out too. That was the code of the dirt trackers. Somebody knocked you off, you returned the compliment next time out, then it was forgotten.

By the end of season he was almost ready for a regular backmarker grading.

He learned to pick off the bunnies in front: go in wide, make a long corner, switch back. Or divebomb up the inside.

Or simply trust in Bongo to supply the extra power and surge down the straight. His peaked helmet was regularly seen at the front of the field.

The pair had even made a couple of trips to Eldura Motordrome, 400 miles south, where the track was designed for cars and was only occasionally utilised by the solos, as the bikes were called. It was fascinating experience for fast-learning Jacko.

The track surface was hard-baked clay, not deep dirt. Speedway folk called this a slick track, one with little, if any, loose top surface. It was fine for Jacko. With his rocket starting technique, there was less grip for a rival to get the drift and drop on him.

And nobody, not even the Clapton international, could regularly outstart Jacko. His reflexes were clearly something out of the ordinary.

Wild and wonderful stories about English speedway whirred around the pit area.

His fellow backmarkers, who had been around, reckoned he was ready for the big adventure across the world.

"But I don't know anyone in Brisbane, never mind Britain," said Jacko.

No worries. You only needed to be an Aussie with a bike in Britain and your world was a bucket of East Coast oysters.

Jacko realised this new life had all but laid the ghosts of his memory; 12,000 miles further on, he believed, they might vanish forever.

Financially he'd squared up Bongo for his loyal support and mechanical magic. His chum could not contemplate such a trip, he gloomily said, being locked into the family business, the only son and all that.

But Jacko was all fired up with ambition, by the idea of Britain, speedway racing and the promise it held.

The fire was still glowing brightly when he set foot on Essex scrubland on that miserable March day while the Waffen SS of Hitler's bodyguard were noisily swilling beer in the kellers of Old Vienna.

ON THE MAPS of the London area he had studied, West Ham was the nearest track to his disembarkation at Tilbury.

Jacko was amazed to realise there were five different London speedways within a twenty-mile circle, all on something called the London Underground.

He didn't know of that many tracks in the whole of Australia.

Leaving his bike in the docks freighting department to be collected later, he hopped aboard a train which clickety-clacked through the startlingly green countryside, with Jacko admiring the plump, pretty, black and white cattle and then gaping through steamed-up windows at the suburban development, which all looked like a concrete termite nest.

The chill March English weather hit him with the impact of a charging water buffalo. He'd hardly acclimatised as the freighter had chugged into Northern waters and climes. The trains did not seem to be heated.

His first experience of this London Underground was a revelation.

No, you didn't get off at West Ham for West Ham Stadium. You needed Plaistow.

Jacko walked down the tight, bustling sidewalks of London's Dockland until arriving at what he considered to be a towering fortress from another age.

West Ham Stadium was bloody gigantic.

Inside was a cement canyon, hundreds of steps up huge terraces and a vast covered stand stretching right down one side, with an unusual lattice-patterned frontispiece. It looked capable of housing the entire population of the Northern Territory.

Although late morning, there was obviously something happening. Frowning men, all in trilbys or flat caps, most with stopwatches, watched with slitted eyes, unspeaking, as beautifully coordinated greyhounds paced the wide raceway.

"Dog trials," explained a Stadium employee, shovelling at a mountain of rubbish.

Jacko had never seen greyhound racing. He seemed to recall it was banned in Aussie. The hounds moved quite superbly; there was poetry in their movement although he thought they must be pretty daft to chase a bundle of fluff on a rail.

Later in his working life at the bottom of the heap in London stadia Jacko would learn of the delights of a 'live kill' to sharpen up the longdogs. This was the banned practice of giving a greyhound a live prey to chase and kill. It would make Jacko sick and angry.

The speedway track was inside the greyhound circuit. It looked a picture: wide, perfectly banked, great shape, measuring 440 yards around, 30-feet wide.

A man could surely give it the gun here, really wind up the throttle.

Jacko was directed up two-dozen cement steps to the rear of the main stand to the speedway manager's office.

He was an explosive little guy with a foghorn voice, an extravagant hat and apparently a legend, known fondly as 'The Admiral of Barking Creek'.

He had been the bloke who had virtually invented speedway back in Australia fifteen years previously and helped introduce the spectacle in Britain a decade earlier.

He looked kindly on Jacko, a fellow Aussie adventurer and said: "I'd like to help you, son. But my Hammers won the league last season and the folk will string me from a Limehouse lamp-post if I change the side this year. I just haven't got room for you.

"But try Wimbledon. Ask for Ralph Greenhalgh, who runs the show. Say I sent you. He's a good friend. Almost jumped off Tower Bridge in despair last year and was signing Yanks and Continentals and just about anyone who could straddle a saddle."

The rascally little 'Admiral' chortled with great good humour and added: "He still finished bottom, though."

Wimbledon Stadium was another revelation. Like the Hammers' circuit it sat squatly right in the middle of teeming urban sprawl, with pretentious-looking terraced houses clambering all over each other. But while West Ham had a cavernous character, Wimbledon had clean-cut, art deco lines. The track, again sited inside a greyhound circuit, looked a bit of a challenge. The lap distance was a hundred yards shorter than West Ham, with wickedly tighter turns.

Ralph Greenhalgh was tall, ramrod straight like the Guardsman he once had been, and wore an impressive Homburg hat along with an air of distain. Despite his appearance, he was a calculating, in-fighting track promotion campaigner and knew only too well that frequently these raggle-taggle Australian kids often had potential box office gold dust in the seat of their pants.

"I'll give you a couple of second halves," he said. "And we're short of ground staff so there's a bit of a job for you there if you've nowhere else to go.

"You can sleep in the watchman's hut and have a shower in the dressing room. But only after race nights. I can't have you wasting hot water every day."

So Jacko Rintzen joined Wimbledon, by no means an overnight sensation. But he was overwhelmed. It was a completely new world. He might as well have been on Speedway Planet Saturn. When he walked around his new place of employment, his eyes grew wider. The stairs of the main stand seemed to be marble. There was a restaurant where diners could watch racing in luxury behind a huge glass frontage. Racing would appear like moving wallpaper.

The toilets, which he would have to clean, were all gleaming white tiles, fresh smelling, immaculate. Jacko would not have been surprised to see the King of England perched regally on the porcelain. In the outback, Jacko took a short-handled shovel into the dunes when he needed to go. I could live quite happily in here, he thought.

His problem about retrieving his equipment from the docks freight store was solved when bossman Greenhalgh revealed there was a stadium service vehicle heading for Tilbury to pick up a load of Dutch bulbs and special fertiliser from Rotterdam. "Go with the driver, stick your equipment in with that load," he said, with massive disinterest. No way would the Wimbledon chief trust Jacko to take the wagon on his own. He had known itinerant Australians who had disappeared without trace if you left them with a back tyre.

So Jacko's machine and equipment, his only worldly goods, arrived at the Wimbledon workshops stacked on what appeared to be bags of cow manure. Jacko couldn't imagine why a stadium wanted special flower bulbs and fertisilser. The morosely uncommunicative driver simply said: "Decoration, innit?" England was surely full of surprises.

The racing format, too, was a revelation.

There were no handicaps. It was team racing: eight to a team, four in a race, two from each team. That was the week-to-week format. But there was also individual racing and championships, where each man had four or five starts and the highest points-scorer triumphed.

Standard points-scoring was three for a win, two for second, one for third, nothing for a last place.

British tracks had electronic starting grids with harder surfaces than he had previously experienced. Track surfaces were cinders or factory waste and could be six inches deep.

After each league match, there were the 'second halves' that Greenhalgh had enigmatically promised.

Juniors and hopefuls like Jacko were given a couple of starts. The best two would then be matched with the lower order reserves from the league sides. The team members would then have a second half knockout tournament and a successful junior or reserve might get a replacement outing in that event.

The martinet Greenhalgh wouldn't contemplate giving Jacko any practice laps. "Practice day was ten days ago, boy," he said curtly.

Programme format meant Jacko had to watch the entire league match from the pits enclosure, which spilled out onto the exterior greyhound circuit at Wimbledon's Plough Lane, SW17 arena.

The show itself was simply startling.

Wimbledon was bathed in floodlighting, a first for Jacko. The centre green was dotted with illuminated flower beds. "Got it, that's what the load from Tilbury was for," thought Jacko. The track staff, graders and starting-line attendants, all identically dressed in Wimbledon's red and yellow colours, marched into the arena with the precision of a brigade of Grenadiers. All the pits staff were in newly laundered white overalls.

The atmosphere was a fired-up fairyland: terraces jam-packed with fans wielding rattles, bells, red and yellow scarves. There was a sea of heads wherever Jacko looked, there were hundreds crammed into the bars and cafeterias dotted around the top of the terraces.

A dance band crooner warbled loudly about The Folks Who Live On The Hill over the tannoy while the fans sang and swayed with the music.

There was surely nothing in the world like British speedway.

Jacko ached to have Bongo at his side, sharing this astounding spectacle. What a tale he would have for him.

Funny he should think of Bongo at a time like this.

He stood, looking left towards the starting gate for the first heat and as the four riders were unleashed, he turned another mental somersault.

They seemed to be broadside on from the moment they left the tapes.

It was sheer spectacle. No wonder speedway had survived the Depression, the Talkies, the Abdication and was rivalling Charlie Chaplin and soccer for audience appeal in London.

The nine-day wonder had become a nine-year sensation.

After the league match, it was the second half of the programme, when juniors like Jacko were given their opportunity. Jacko and his fellow juniors had been supplied with an elasticated helmet cover and a matching body colour. That was the method of rider identification. The colours were red, blue, white and yellow. Starting gate positions were decided by the pits marshal with a device they called the shaker.

Four similarly coloured balls were shaken then dropped to the bottom of the box. Riders started in the sequence they fell, from the inside to out.

It was a time-honoured ritual. Jacko quickly gauged how important the gate position would be on this tight, twisting track, with three rivals level with him on the line.

He drew yellow and was allocated gate four, the outside. That was a plus. A clean break should guarantee a clear run around the first turn.

Jacko sneaked in a half-throttle practice lap. A couple of cheerful types in the pits had advised him about the correct gear ratio. Speedway bikes had a fixed gear, in Britain between 8.5 and 9.3 to one. Wimbledon being smallish required a low gearing. Jacko hoped he'd got it right.

When his race started, he banged out the clutch and was immediately confronted by a front wheel that was rearing and bucking and a rear end snaking like some maddened mustang being broken. The harder surface starting grid was a whole new proposition.

Jacko's intuitive balance and control maintained his contact with the machine and he powered after his rivals, who seemed almost to have disappeared.

For the remainder of the race, Jacko was battling to avoid the fence, which came rushing up to him at every turn.

At the chequered flag, he realised there was only one rider ahead of him. The other two had slid off somewhere during the race. Jacko hadn't noticed them. Apparently falls and general motorised mayhem were traditional in junior events.

In his second outing, he kept the revs down to prevent wild front wheel looping(wheelie-ing, as they said) and missed the jump completely.

Again he managed to avoid the fence for four laps and discovered somebody else had conveniently bitten the dust.

A third place.

He hadn't caused the headline writers to splosh printing ink over the billboards. Yet. But he'd earned a quid and with the two pounds ten ground staff wages promised by Mr. Greenhalgh for sweeping the terraces, he calculated he'd enough to feed himself for a week.

He'd lapped up the atmosphere and experience and couldn't wait for more.

THE NEXT WEEK brought another experience for Jacko.

Rain.

It drizzled steadily in fine old English style all day and by the time Jacko was called into action, the surface looked like a mudhole of molasses.

This presented a completely new headache. The outside grid became a grease patch because this was the racing line the riders chose down the straight.

After his first experience of attempting to go from nought to forty-five miles an hour in thirty yards on a harder surface, Jacko realised he had to master an amended starting technique.

Only one place to practice: in the Wimbledon Stadium carpark – where he'd already made dozens of starts until either running out of dope or being hounded away by irate near-residents bitching about the racket.

Now, however, another problem. A hard, slippery surface.

Jacko watched the blokes drawn on the outside spinning crazily while the inside grids accelerated steadily away. Fortunately in his first race he had been drawn in two, got to the first corner with shoulders on either side, knocked off the throttle and more or less scooted around the apex.

There were junior riders all over the track in various heaps by the time he crept over the finishing line still upright for his first race win in the capital of the British Empire.

His control kept him aboard on his second outing for another very tentative four laps and second placing.

Many seasoned campaigners were not enthusiastic about getting their backsides wet in the conditions, so Jacko was given two more starts. Adapting cautiously to conditions, he resisted the natural temptation to twist the throttle to its maximum.

He picked up another third place, delighted that he hadn't been completely tailed off at the rear by his opponents, for they were all team members. Best of all, he had accumulated over a tenner, the first time he'd had a double-figure pay packet.

Now he only had to be as successful every night of the week for the next ten years to be able to buy the Simpson Desert.

Mr Greenhalgh grunted: "Well, at least you seem capable of staying on for four laps. I'd better put you on a contract."

So Jacko signed three different-coloured contract forms with Wimbledon Stadium Ltd, which were counter-signed and lodged with the Auto Cycle Union in its stately HQ sited within an exhaust echo of Buckingham Palace.

Jacko was on his way.

CHAPTER 4

BUT THE WAY, though paved with brave intentions and grouted with enthusiasm, was not an easy one.

Jacko continued to get a regular second-half outing at Plough Lane and, with his toils on the ground staff, he scratched out an existence. He raised enough spare cash to acquire a rough old greatcoat. He was still finding England bone-crackingly cold.

Although his riding style was adapting well to British conditions, he quickly realised his speedway engine was not prepared efficiently and fast enough to make competitive progress. He badly missed Bongo's magic touch and could not afford to shell out for a decent mechanic in SW17.

Desperately he mixed in with the grease-stained gang in the Wimbledon workshops, always asking advice, endeavouring to steal the odd wrinkle, trying to sharpen his machinery. He tried every wheeze he'd overheard: including boiling his chains in oil to make them more supple. He stripped down his motor and cleaned every part furiously. He paid meticulous attention to the clutch plates and the fuel feed. There were wry tales about one bloke whose carb kept playing up and after a couple of weeks had found a dead woodlouse blocking an inlet.

But for all his diligence, Jacko knew for certain he was no mechanical maestro. He swiftly got the message that he was cut out to deliver the milk, not pull the cart.

Week after week when he eased the throttle to flat out, rivals were still going away from him.

There were problems with tyres, too.

Some blokes fitted a new rear tyre every meeting. Jacko could barely afford one a month. It meant he was a spinner, not a winner. He was drifting into mediocrity on non-competitive equipment.

The awful truth hit him like a silent movies custard pie on the night, getting late into the season, when he landed what should have been his comic-book big break.

One of the Wimbledon team regulars had cracked a collar bone and he had been drafted into the team at reserve.

He was thrilled it was a match away at West Ham. He was bursting to give those big raking turns, the first he had clapped eyes on in British speedway, a real blast.

Hogan's ghost: there must have been 35,000 salty East Enders shoe-horned into that yawning arena.

Old Foghorn, the bossman who'd been so sympathetic to Jacko, was famed for his outrageous showmanship at the Docklands arena. Dancing girls, marching bands, Russian Cossacks, elephants, camel races, he'd even tried to stage a race between the locally based greyhounds and a cheetah. Jacko would have loved to have seen that. Foghorn's riders made a ritual of burning his hat on the centre green.

It was always a carnival with Old Foghorn.

But it wasn't all the fun of the fair for Jacko.

He was given four starts, loved every inch of the quarter-mile track, and had sixteen spectacular laps blazing away around the outside line – getting pretty much nowhere.

Conditions were the nearest to his home track at Baranga. But every time Jacko went roaring up on the fence exiting the sweeping corners, the opposition simply motored away from him down the straights.

The crowd lapped up his efforts. He was spectacular, he was exciting. He received nearly as much applause as the race winners, although he was a little-known visitor.

Even the announcer said: "Jacko Rintzen at the back there, working his heart out for nothing."

Not nothing really, thought Jacko. I'm still getting paid for four starts that I wasn't expecting.

The big, big star in the crossed-Hammers body colours that night was a nuggetty, flame-haired little Aussie called Bluey Wilkinson. Jacko watched him in awe. He was the complete goods. He was winning races effortlessly by the length of the straight, still going away from the opposition. He made it look easy.

He lifted Jacko's spirits in the dressing rooms after racing, nudging him, giving a sideways grin and saying: "Hard tack, kid. Reckon if you got a decent motor, I'd have to watch for you."

The West Ham dressing rooms, deep in the bowels of the main stand, had two enormous baths, one for each team. Jacko had never seen anything like them. They were like swimming pools. He'd never bathed with anyone else before.

While he was wallowing, listening to the cheerful banter of the other steaming riders, Old Foghorn entered cautiously; he'd ended up fully clothed in that bath before.

"Good show, son," he growled to Jacko. "The crowd loved you. They know and love a genuine trier in East London.

"I always keep a fiver for what I call 'crash bonus' which I give to any nut who I reckon has entertained the crowd going ass over tip. You've earned it tonight." And he dropped a white five-pound note into the bath water.

Jacko's first bonus.

But it wasn't his last from West Ham that year.

OVER 93,000 fanatics, the greatest crowd yet known in speedway, squeezed into Empire Stadium, Wembley, for the 1938 World Championship Final – and Jacko was one of them. Mr Greenhalgh had arranged a charabanc from the Wimbledon carpark, where Jacko so often practised his starts, to take the odds and sods of stadium staff to the most important event of the speedway year.

It was only a dozen miles to Wembley around the South, then North Circular roads, but such was the traffic converging on Empire Stadium that the chara left three hours before the first race. Jacko had never seen such gridlock. Three hours to cover twelve miles! A man could cover over a hundred miles of outback in that time.

Wembley Stadium, built for the Empire Exhibition in the same year speedway was born, was the showpiece of the booming twentieth-century British stadia cult.

West Ham and Wimbledon might have been startlingly impressive. But his first sight of Wembley completely floored Jacko.

Looking directly down Wembley Way thronged with fans, Empire Stadium dominated the landscape and hovered majestically, like the kind of mirage which hardened station hands insisted a bloke imagined if he was lost in the desert and mad with thirst.

Jacko decided it was the greatest spectacle a man could expect to see.

There must have been 500 coaches, cars and motor bikes as far as the eye stretched in the carparks. Jacko climbed 200 stairs at least to reach his seat way up between the iconic Twin Towers.

From his seat he looked down around at the bowl-shaped cauldron of raucous colourful speedway folk who were creating an atmosphere unequalled in any realm of sporting spectacle.

Even the Wembley boss, the highly respected Arthur Elvin, had special status, extra class. Not that Jacko agreed with Sir Arthur's insistence on having all the competitors listed in the Wembley programme with their full Christian names. So away went all the lovely speedway Tigers and Bronchos and Sliders and even Bills and Berts. Instead, awfully respectable Williams and Herberts were paraded.

If ever I get to ride Wembley I'll be listed as Jon Rintzen, mulled Jacko impishly. Nobody had ever, ever called him that. It would be one helluva joke if the revered Wembley supremo was the first to call him his proper name.

From his seat above the starting gate he looked to his left down past the cascade of seating to the pits on the apex of the third and fourth turns. The sixteen finalists were harboured at the end of the North Bend Tunnel, which burrowed back into the dressing rooms. Wedged around the pits and the North Bank was a sea of red, blue and white Hammers. The West Ham End. They were singing for their Bluey Wilkinson, every man, jack and jill of them.

He could hear the staccato, unsynchronised thrum and throb of warming motors above the expectant buzz of the crowd. It sounded like an immense colony of lions howling for their dinner. Even way up in the Gods of the main stand the air wafted with burning methanol. Jacko could smell speedway.

The centre green of the arena, the famed Wembley turf, was emerald and immaculate. The massed bands of His Majesty's Brigade of Guards in their scarlet tunics and black bearskins looked like clockwork toys, breaking beautifully from slow into quick marchtime. It was impressive and stirring and Jacko was impressed and stirred. Hell, those Hitler and Mussolini blokes they were all worried about must be nutty to want to take on such splendidly disciplined soldiery.

By the starting gate, on raised platforms, were two trumpeters, in gold-braided uniforms, ready to blast crisp fanfares for every race. They were spotlighted by crossed beams, aimed way up in the upper reaches of this incredible structure.

A sudden lull, spine-chilling silence, then the roaring sound of the march-time Entry of the Gladiators engulfed the terraces as the finalists, tiny and only just identifiable, stepped into main stage.

Jacko felt the hairs on the back of his neck stiffen.

This wasn't just sporting spectacle. This was theatre.

The arena was a riot, a whirligig of team colours, flags and banners of rival track followers.

Around him on the home straight, a huge splurge of red and white with black Lions rampant. The Wembley supporters. Elvin's Lions were the most famous, glamorous outfit in the world. Way to his left, a sea of orange and black from New Cross, south of the river, blending like a water painting into the red and yellow of Wimbledon.

Down the back straight, the Harringay fans overlapped the red, black and white of Belle Vue (Manchester), with their huge placards of the Ace of Clubs. That was their feared emblem and they clearly thought they were...the ace of clubs.

Hammer-mania on the pits corner. There were Bristol banners and even Hackney, who hadn't even operated at senior level that year.

Bells, whirring rattles, and at least half a dozen bugles, vying with each other with fruity calls that would have stirred the loins of the Light Brigade to charge. National flags, too: Union Jacks, Stars and Stripes, a few proud blue Aussie flags. Jacko mused that speedway racing seemed to be a sport exclusive to the English-speaking nations. At least, its World Championship Final was.

This was surely a once-in-a-lifetime experience.

The twenty heats went by in a whirl, a blink.

Although Wimbledon had three finalists, two were Americans that Mr Greenhalgh had drafted in to fire up his fortunes: Wilbur Lamoreaux and Benny Kaufman. They were decent blokes, smart riders, stars, but didn't have a lot to do with groundstaff junior snot like Jacko.

He found himself firmly behind Bluey (listed as Arthur in the programme) Wilkinson, the superstar who'd had time for a word of encouragement in the West Ham dressing room.

Everyone agreed that Wilkinson should have been crowned champion two years earlier, in the first official staging of the World Championship.

He had been unbeaten at that Wembley Final, but the organisers had arranged some harebrained scheme which saw finalists carry qualifying bonus points from earlier rounds into the meeting. Bluey had been robbed because he had one fewer than the declared winner, another Australian, a dashing, matinee idol type called Lionel Van Praag.

On this purple night for Jacko, justice was done. Wilkinson reeled off four straight race wins and looked poetry in motion. The complete speedway rider.

Although beaten by the reigning champion, American Jack Milne, in the penultimate race, Wilkinson's fourteen points were sufficient to crown him the third official king of world speedway.

As tradition demanded, the first three riders paraded for the screaming, celebrating fans perched on the front of the Wembley tractor used for pulling the grader over the cindery surface.

It was an eruption of noise and colour.

For the umpteenth time on this sensational September evening, Jacko's neck hairs rose. This, this was the very heart, soul and lifeblood of living experience. He would never forget this night, this high-octane occasion.

And he wanted his very own share of it.

Even as the stadium emptied Jacko still sat spellbound, drinking in the last dregs of the atmosphere.

It took him over fifteen minutes to sort out his directions and locate the Wimbledon staff coach.

They were late leaving, so got stuck in the tortured, stop-go traffic all the way up to Neasden Cross. The coach was wedged in with dozens of others, in two, sometimes three lanes, inching forward.

They edged up alongside one coach festooned in red, blue and white with huge Hammers flags draped the entire length of the vehicle. On the chilling, late evening air, Jacko heard the passengers roaring a strange song:

I'm forever blowing bubbles.
Pretty bubbles in the air.
They fly so high, nearly reach the sky.
Then like my dreams they fade and die.

The bloke sitting next to Jacko explained this was the West Ham anthem, adopted from the Hammers' soccer neighbours, who did not attract anything like as many followers as the speedmen. Jacko was not aware there was a West Ham soccer team, never mind a team anthem.

"Funny sort of song for a footy crowd, isn't it?" He said to his informant. "How d'they get hold of that?"

"Oh, it was something to do with when the new soccer stadium was opened back in the 20s" was the reply. "They had a little boy with a mop of blond curls who modelled in adverts for Pears soap. He was nicknamed Bubbles. He performed the first kick off and the East End crowd serenaded him with "I'm forever blowing bubbles".

"It's just sort of stuck".

The bubble-blowing West Ham singers spotted Jacko in his window seat and yelled across: "Wotcher, Jacko. Yer turn for the title next, mate. You can do it."

Jacko was stunned by their recognition and sentiment and permitted himself a luxury fantasy.

Jeez, wouldn't it be really something to win the World Championship for these wonderful folk? And have them singing for me?.

Right then he vowed to himself: I won't let my dreams fade and die.

CHAPTER 5

ON THE TRACK, Jacko just about survived 1938.

Off track, he thrived.

Ever the willing worker, he laboured long around Wimbledon Stadium. He must have swept up and dumped a hundred tons of rubbish. He gathered so many torn-up Tote tickets, sad souvenirs of misplaced avarice, it put him off betting forever.

But it was the greyhound racing staff that clasped Jacko to their hearts.

Clearly, he had a special way with the dogs. All the dogs loved Jacko, rolled over for him, furiously wagged their ridiculously long tails at the very sight of him. In the kennels, they loped to be at his feet.

It was the kennel master, a stern, bulky type always in a black bowler and voluminous belted mac, who admitted: "If that boy stood by the finishing line, the hounds would knock three spots off their fastest time getting to him."

He suggested Jacko move into the rough accommodation above the stadium's kennels, where all the graded dogs were housed. These were sited on a spare half-acre abutting Wimbledon Common, half a mile from the track.

Jacko moved in alongside Ruthie and Doll, the two resident kennel maids: cheery, robust girls in jodhpurs who had no apparent roots or ties. They secretly kept as pets a couple of old dogs who were past racing. One lovable, elderly old fellow only had one eye. They called him Nelson.

Jacko asked the girls what happened to all the other old greyhounds once they finished racing.

"You don't want to know, mate," grimaced Ruthie.

A few kindly owners kept them as pets, fewer still found a benefactor who paid for their keep in a dog's home. The rest? Ruthie pulled a sad face, and put two fingers, gun-like to her head.

Jacko got the message and thought a great deal about it

The dogs were Ruthie and Doll's life, their all-consuming passion. When they saw Jacko's way with them, they adopted him too.

He brushed, groomed and fed the dogs. He even grabbed a blanket and slept with them in the straw when they were whelping or had a bout of kennel sickness. It was no hardship for Jacko to doss down on hard boards but Ruthie and Doll and even the kennel master admired his dedication and concern.

In his spare time, Jacko devoured newspapers, books and magazines.

He became aware every country in Europe seemed to hate the next one and was hellbent on wiping it off the map. Then the English Prime Minister, who looked like an undertaker, kept chuntering on about 'peace in our time'.

There was much ado about the Test cricket. The girls went all gooey about a dashing English type called Denis Compton scoring his first Test century. But just up the road at Kennington Oval, it was a bloke called Hutton who got all the runs. In the measured opinion of his stadium workmates and the workshops crew, the Aussie Bradman was the real 'guvnor'.

Jacko was impressed to learn that the first England–Australia speedway Test had been staged at Wimbledon eight years previously to coincide with a cricket Test at The Oval. The speedway attracted a bigger crowd than the cricket.

He was also rapt to read a line in the Speedway News magazine that described him as 'promising, talented with a big future'.

Which was all very fine but at the end of the speedway season in October, as Jews were being hounded all over Europe, the Japanese were occupying Canton and Orson Welles was scaring the US stiff with a radio report about an invasion from space, Jacko had to face the fact there was no way he could afford to go back to Australia.

What little extra money he had managed to find he sent back to Bongo in Baranga to pay off the JAP bike he had given him. But he wasn't homesick. And the greyhound folk welcomed him staying for the winter.

On the chilly winter evenings, Jacko joined Ruthie and Doll listening to dance band music on a wheezy old wireless. They were like a couple of jolly sisters. And they nursed him with some foul but effective remedy when he picked up his first stinking English cold. The winter weather initially creased Jacko. He was accustomed to the desert getting chilly at night, but suburban London had a damp, clinging cold that turned his bonemarrow to marshmallow. The girls found him several spare pairs of old overalls to wear. Ruthie knitted him a woolly hat and produced a hideous garment they called longjohns, which he wore in bed. Resilient Jacko became weatherproof.

Ruthie and Doll insisted on taking him out and introduced him to the great English passion of going to the pictures.

It was an amazing ritual. You queued outside this emporium that looked like it had been designed for some madcap monarch. When you eventually got in, you stood at the back until a seat became free in an atmosphere blue with tobacco smoke with folk coughing their guts up all around.

It was a great treat for the girls. They adored musicals.

"You've got hips just like Fred Astaire, Jacko," they teased.

At the end of the movie, after the cinema mysteriously played the National Anthem they strolled to an all-night open air refreshment van where Jacko bought them steaming mugs of tea and corned beef sandwiches. Jacko preferred cheese.

"Oooh, Jacko, you are lovely, treating us like this," they said. "All the other boys just want to shag you then sod off."

On occasional nights, they would bring fish and chips, the great English speciality, wrapped in old copies of the News Chronicle, back to their rooms above the kennels.

Jacko was into fish and chips. He didn't have the same hang-ups about eating fish as he did about meat. There were, he reasoned, a great many fish around Australia which, given the opportunity, would eat him. And considering the monstrous cannibalism that went on daily under the ocean since time began, Jacko reckoned his bit of battered cod wasn't going to make much difference.

Increasingly Ruthie and Doll treated Jacko like a slightly helpless kid brother. "We've got to tidy you up," said Ruthie. She had worked as a seamstress in a sweat shop in the Walworth Road before devoting her life to greyhounds. She and Doll acquired Jacko a newer, more modern set of racing leathers after they had backed the winner of an open race at Catford.

"I shall tailor them to fit you perfectly," said Ruthie, an absolute whiz on a sewing machine. "We've got to show off your snake hips, haven't we?"

"Aw, I don't want to stand out, bring attention on myself," protested Jacko, skittishly.

But Ruthie was off and stitching. She tapered the hips and leggings, built up square, studded shoulders, then cleverly patched in chequered epaulettes in red

45

and yellow, Wimbledon's colours. Compared to most of his shapeless speedway contemporaries, Jacko, to his embarrassment, stood out stylishly.

Ruthie had one more loving gimmick for Jacko. All speedmen wore goggles and covered their nose and mouths with face scarves which they knotted behind their crash helmets. A rider needed protection from flying cinders and dust, although there were stories of teeth being knocked out like broken piano keyboards.

Ruthie bought Jacko a white, silk evening evening scarf, like she had seen Fred Astaire wearing in Top Hat and Shall We Dance, then personalised it brilliantly, stitching intricately a horse and dog head motif linked in thread. "Your friends," she said to Jacko. The dog's head looked nothing like Blue. But Blue didn't look like any other dog, thought Jacko, touched deeply. Apart from Kerslake giving him Bowz and Bongo's generosity, these were the first gifts Jacko had received. The first from any female. "I'll always wear it, always," he promised a beaming Ruthie.

At Christmas and New Year, the girls and other stadium staff bundled him around to their local pub, the White Lion.

The pub was dominated by stadium, speedway and greyhound folk. They called it the White Line – the term for the inside marker on the speedway track. A rider was excluded if he allowed two wheels to cross the line. The girls loved what they called a 'knees up'.

Jacko didn't care much for the beer. He hated not being in control of his faculties. But the girls swilled gin and orange until their cheeks went rosy and they bellowed out songs about cruising dahn the river and Enery The Eighth and lyrics that Jacko simply could not comprehend.

Oh, we all got blue blind paralytic drunk
When the Old Dun Cow caught fire.

Jacko realised he was not a young man of music.

He also realised, to his considerable surprise, that he was becoming comfortable, cosy and settled in his new lifestyle.

There was a new speedway season approaching.

He still had everything to prove.

WHITE FLAGS were hoisted all over Madrid to signal the end of the Spanish Civil War the day Jacko seriously attacked his track career again in 1939.

He had his first ride at Wimbledon without a single practice lap. But this time around he was ready a week in advance for official practice day and almost needed to be forcibly removed from the track, spending lap after lap trying new racing lines, practising start after start.

"Somebody go and haul that boy off the track," ordered Mr Greenhalgh.

Nobody cared much about Jacko. Furious furore raged around Plough Lane because Mr. Greenhalgh had splashed out thousands of pounds, an unimaginable amount, to bring speedway's boy wonder to Wimbledon.

Bryan Corbin was a half-pint South Coast kid who had hogged all the headlines because he had graduated from riding a push bike on backlot tracks to qualify for a World Speedway Final in less than two years.

Because he had tiny legs and stood little over five feet, everyone called him Nipper. He looked like a third-form schoolboy and had famously once been thrown out of a pits area for being apparently 'too young'.

He called everyone 'moosh'(except Mr. Greenhalgh whom he called 'Guv'nor'), was notorious for always ordering egg and chips for supper, had a wonderfully easy-going nature, was a quite beautifully balanced motorcyclist, and he formed an immediate bond with Jacko, who was the same age. They were an odd couple: Nipper short, stubby, aggressively confident, full of cheeky chatter; Jacko, lean, elegant in movement, reticent, never pushy.

A track tactician with natural ability, Nipper was also a cocky showman whom crowds everywhere adored: his party piece was to tear off his racing goggles when he was leading and toss them nonchalantly to his mechanic at the pits fence.

Quite unintentionally, Jacko had also developed a unique habit, although showmanship was the last thing on his mind. As he cruised to the starting line, he repeatedly took both hands off the handlebars to adjust his goggles and Ruthie's silk scarf. It was second nature to him to ride with no hands after his months of training under Kerslake's demanding eye when learning horsemanship. He would naturally regrip the handlebars at the start.

"Oughta be in a bleedin' display team, moosh," said Nipper. "Stealing my thunder."

"Wasn't even aware I was doing it," replied Jacko

The mechanic in the pits who safely pouched Nipper's goggles as he sailed by was the greatly respected Jim Chinnock from Southampton. 'Chinners', a master tuner with a knack of apparently listening intently to every mechanical suggestion from a rider and then doing approximately the opposite, was rumoured to sleep in his grease-stained overalls

When he had a rare spare moment, Chinners 'breathed' on Jacko's ageing JAP.

He immediately felt the benefit.

Safety fences did not come roaring up to him quite so horrifically and by the end of the first month of the 1939 season he had forced his way into the Wimbledon team in a reserve berth. He was now getting National League payrates and able to afford a couple of hot meals a day.

It was a bonus being paired with Nipper in races.

As a reserve, Jacko learned that more established team partners expected, indeed demanded, choice of starting positions.

In league racing, teams alternated gates, with pairings going off either one and three, or two and four grids.

Jacko became used to being palmed off with the dodgiest gate. Senior team-mates would simply grunt: "I'll take one" or "I'll go outside."

But not Nipper.

About starting positions, he would say: "You choose, moosh. Then go like bollocks and I'll cover you."

Nipper was brilliant at everything, particularly team riding – covering your partner's back to ensure maximum points from the race. If Jacko could make the start, Nipper would miraculously appear on his back wheel coming out of the second turn and nurse him past the winning line like a sharp-witted sheepdog.

They were paired together at West Ham, where Jacko was again given a warm reception and repeated his blazing, wide-riding routine. But this year his motor was a bit sharper and with Nipper somehow protecting his inside on every corner, the Dons managed an away victory.

The Hammers were not the force they had been. Wonderful Wilkinson had retired after one match to become promoter at Sheffield. Jacko would never achieve a personal ambition to beat the little ginger genius.

He rode with Nipper at the tiny 262-yard 'Frying Pan' at New Cross, just off the Old Kent Road – Ruthie and Doll had a song about knocking 'em dahn the Old Kent Road.

It certainly wasn't a full throttle, full locker track. Nipper almost got off and carried Jacko home in a couple of races. "Good fun, innit," said Nipper, with his schoolboy grin.

Jacko went north for the first time to Manchester, miles and miles from London; and so many houses. He could hardly believe the setting for the famous Belle Vue club. It was part of an amusement park complex, set in a maze of cobbled streets with tiny terraced houses, all with chimneys belching coal fumes and kids in bare feet and rags playing hopscotch on the pavements.

Nipper loved Belle Vue.

Beyond the first and second corners of the perfectly shaped, wide, 418-yard natural raceway was the amusement park Big Dipper – 'The Bobs' as it was known by the locals.

Before racing, Nipper insisted on riding The Bobs for twenty minutes non-stop. Jacko felt he had left his stomach floating on the Lancastrian air after the first five minutes.

"After that, moosh, speedway is a piece of cake," Nipper said.

The Belle Vue Zoo, incorporated into the park, also had an elephant, the first Jacko had ever seen.

The jumbo lumbered straight over to him and wrapped his trunk lovingly around his shoulders.

"Blimey, never seen him do that before," said his keeper.

Nipper was enormously impressed.

"Bleeding Nature Boy, you are," he said.

Although Belle Vue was a terrific racing track, the Aces team were a bunch of murderous mongrels, whose language seemed all 'ayes', 'reets' and 'boogers', who hit you from all angles on the track.

Jacko had a tough night.

But he was learning all the time.

He also realised he was really loving this harum-scarum, easy-come, easy-go gypsy lifestyle.

He was in his element when either sitting in the dressing room, hanging around in the workshops, or splashing about in the communal bath with his team-mates, listening to the wild and wonderful stories and tall tales which circulated within speedway, all the yarns being accompanied by hoarse yaks of laughter and hoots of disbelief.

First World Champion Lionel Van Praag had once held up a bank with a toy pistol for a laugh. Two blokes in the New Cross team swore they had seen the ghost of Robin Hood where the Sherwood Forest fringed the A1 coming home from Newcastle. A ghost in evening wear had regularly been identified in the upper tiers of the main stand at West Ham, a spectre of the speedway rather than phantom of the opera.

Daft Phil Bishop swam ashore in his England blazer when the liner carrying the international team to Australia had anchored off Aden and had nearly been eaten by two sharks. Billy 'Cyclone' Lamont was wildly rumoured to have had an enormous grass track racing pile-up and landed on the back of a cow in a neighbouring field.

Eric Spencer once raced the clock at midnight around Manchester Town Hall, completing the circuit fifteen seconds quicker than it took for the clock to strike twelve.

The first rider to be injured in British racing swallowed a wasp during the 1928 meeting in the Epping Forest. A crazy American called Ray Tauser had done a parachute jump, landing in a coach and four taking two old ladies to church. There was a bloke at Belle Vue who kept his false teeth in his toolbox during races.

One of the Harringay boys ran out of oil in his wagon on the A5 returning from Manchester so topped up his sump with a bottle of Guinness to complete the journey.

Charlie Spinks, one of the original old dirt track Diggers, had demolished an entire shop window proving the ring he had bought for some floozie was a genuine diamond and would cut glass.

There was a track boss in Western Australia who had a five-foot carpet snake as a pet to keep the rats down.

There was a joker who, like Jacko, had hopped a tramper to Britain but who ended up in Santiago.

Jacko was utterly astonished when he heard Mr Greenhalgh had once been the All-England Charleston dancing champion.

The stories and anecdotes were endless. Jacko realised he really felt part of this colourful camaraderie and loved the life he lived.

But that life ended abruptly only four days before the scheduled staging of the 1939 World Final, when Adolf Hitler finally turned the world upside down and the lights went out on London speedway for six years.

Jacko had nowhere near qualified for the Final but Nipper had been one of the favourites for the crown.

Jacko knew he had to head home.

One final tearful visit to a moviedrome monstrosity with Ruthie and Doll to see The Wizard of Oz.

"You know you are our own special Wizard of Aus, Jacko," they said, covering him with embarrassing wet kisses.

Nipper thought he might join the RAF. He fancied himself in one of those Hurricane fighters, but his mum insisted he find a safer job.

"You getting a ship, moosh?" he asked Jacko, after fixing Chinners to mothball his motor for the duration.

Jacko could not afford the fare. Although he had made more money than he had dreamed possible during the curtailed 1939 season, he had given all his savings to Ruthie and Doll to pay for the upkeep of all the old retired greyhounds at Wimbledon for as long as possible.

"Daft bleeder," said Nipper, shaking his head but secretly highly impressed. "How will you get home?"

"Work my passage," said Jacko. "I've done it before."

CHAPTER 6

COMMUNIQUE TO:
OC GHQ Allied Forces, Cairo.
FROM: Brig. E.A. Horsey, OC 2nd Brigade, 9th Division AIF.

I WOULD COMMEND YOUR ATTENTION TO THE CONDUCT OF
11471234 L/CPL J. RINTZEN FOR HIS INITIATIVE AND EXPERTISE AS A
DISPATCH RIDER DURING THE BREAKOUT FROM THE QATTARA DE-
PRESSION DURING THE EL ALAMEIN CAMPAIGN.

SHOWING COMMENDABLE SKILL AND INITIATIVE ON HIS MOTOR-
CYCLE, L/CPL RINTZEN WAS ABLE TO DISTRACT AN AFRIKA KORPS
HEAVY MG POSITION TO ALLOW THREE FELLOW MEMBERS OF THIS
BRIGADE WHO WERE ISOLATED, PINNED DOWN AND IN IMMEDIATE
DANGER OF BEING WIPED OUT, TO ESCAPE BACK TO OUR LINES.

Thus, Jacko Rintzen, reluctant soldier, unwilling cavalryman, became mentioned
in dispatches.

What a laugh, thought Jacko, and all through a trick I perfected in the carpark
at Wimbledon Stadium.

It had taken Jacko nearly a year to get back to Australia. It was almost as crazy as that bloke who ended up in Santiago. His clanky old cargo boat picked up loads from port to port. When she was unloaded, the captain docked up and waited until an agent or merchant turned up another cargo.

Jacko had spent two weeks in the steaming heat of Aden until the ship picked up a load of betel nuts. Eventually he stumbled back to Baranga and shacked up with Bongo and his family. Bel was now married, a mother, and already in the considerable bloom of a second pregnancy. Bongo was now qualified as a mechanic, deeply into the family saddlery business, but simply bursting to get into the great adventure of World War Two.

Now that Jacko was back and he had a pal to join up with, he couldn't wait.

They hopped on a chuffy old train that looked like it had been rattling the lines since the original gold rush days and enlisted in Sydney.

Amazingly, they were first billeted in makeshift accommodation in the bullpens at Sydney Showground, the headquarters of Australian speedway. It was an odd introduction for Jacko to the most iconic speedway arena in the land of his birth, where his hero Bluey Wilkinson was a legend. But Jacko couldn't see much of the actual track. It was packed solid with military vehicles.

All Bongo's visions of the pair fighting shoulder to shoulder together vanished when they were paraded for the personnel selection officer. When the Army saw Bongo's mechanical qualifications he was immediately packed off to the Engineers.

Jacko, whose address was listed as the Baranga cattle station, was viewed disinterestedly by the PSO.

"Stockman, eh?" he said. "You'll be set on the Cavalry or Light Horse."

"No way," replied Jacko.

"But all you jackaroos always want to be with horses."

"I think it's a rotten deal for the horses," said Jacko. "They don't ask to go to war yet blokes have been getting 'em slaughtered for centuries. I just don't want to see a lot of horses suffer and die."

"Jeez, you're freaky," said the PSO. "If you're so bothered about the bloody horses you can go in the poor bloody infantry and watch your fellow man get their blocks knocked off."

So the pair went their separate ways for four years.

Jacko technically became an infantryman but soon adapted to Army life. He was accustomed to roughing it. He was a capable soldier.

It didn't take too long before the Army realised that Jacko, an oddball in many ways, was more than useful with motorcycles. His adjutant had watched speedway at The Showground and Parramatta and was smart enough to know that Jacko was the right type to become a military dispatch rider.

Surprisingly, the Army opened up revelations to Jacko about his life. Stunning revelations that left Jacko reeling.

Old Kerslake, back at the cattle station, had actually signed to become his legal guardian years ago. It was there in black and white on his forces enlistment form.

The Australian Government, in one of its most despicable acts of legislation, had for many years pushed orphans and illegitimate kids into domestic service. They had actually taken Aboriginal children away from their mothers 'to improve their lives'. That's why Jacko hadn't seen any youngsters among the nomadic bunches of Aboriginal drifters he'd sometimes seen around the cattle station.

He regarded Kerslake in a new light. The old bugger had saved him from God knows what and never mentioned it. Suddenly, there was a sort of logic in the interest the cattle baron had shown in him. Maybe he actually had paternal affection for Jacko. Jeez, Kerslake legally his Dad! He would have to front up, talk to him about it. The thought caused Jacko sleepless nights in his hard iron barrackroom bed.

Jacko also discovered that although he had ridden speedway on some of the most famous tracks on the planet, he had never actually passed a driving test.

He endured the amusing indignity of learning to ride a big old beastly service machine and do it 'the Army way'. It was rather like handling a dray horse after the aristocratic thoroughbred performance of a speedway JAP.

But Jacko enjoyed the challenge of feeling the clutch, testing the revs, using the gears, and generally becoming as one with the machine.

He not surprisingly became an accomplished DR. When the 9th Division were posted to the North Africa campaign he was not asked, like most of the Aussies, to go tramping up and down the coast road to Tripoli and Tobruk, but retained at headquarters in Cairo. His skill at picking his way through the teeming streets, with their camels, goats, Bedouins, street traders, potholes and roadworks, and about a million wandering pedestrians, kept him from having to dodge too many bullets.

But when the Eighth Army threw everything at Rommel's Afrika Korps in October 1942, Jacko was attached to a battalion of hardened Tobruk veterans at the southern-most tip of the Qattara Depression on the track to Siwa.

It was his lot to roughride with dispatches from the frontline to brigade or maybe GHQ.

The desert didn't worry him. It was just like home. The hard-baked surface around the Depression reminded him a little of the slick track surface at Eldura.

The Afrika Korps, angry as a stirred-up hornet's nest about not being able to outflank El Alamein, were pouring murderous machinegun fire into a couple of Australian companies, who were becoming isolated in pockets of foxholes.

Jacko was dug in under a sandy dune overhang at battalion headquarters when urgent word came in that three Diggers were cut off, pinned down under withering fire from a hidden enemy machinegun position.

"Jerry's also got mortars just back a way," grimaced a ferrety-faced corporal in a huge slouch hat. "Once they get our blokes range, they're cactus.

"What we need is a distraction for the machinegun nest, so our blokes can leg it back to our lines."

"I'll draw their fire," said Jacko. "Or at least their attention."

He kicked the exhaust inlet off the bulky service motor cycle. The motor without the exhaust was deafening. He twisted to maximum revs. He felt as familiar with this twistgrip as on the surgically sensitive throttle of a speedway bike. After weeks in the saddle eighteen hours a day, he was aboard an old, dear friend.

He tested the clutch until he felt a fractional bite. He wound up the revs again. It was ear-splitting. The Jerry machinegunners must have thought there was a Sherman tank about to emerge from behind the overhang.

Instead, the spectacle of what appeared to be some beerfest carnival trick motor cyclist roaring along on his back wheel.

Jacko had covered thirty yards and was disappearing over a sand dune when the pop-eyed Germans managed to realign and bang off a couple of bursts at the crouching figure.

In the confusion, the three isolated Aussies scampered gratefully back to company lines. As they threw themselves back into safe harbour, Ferret Face scratched his balls and said: "Now that was a sight you don't often see in the bloody desert. A genuine trick cyclist."

Thus Jacko was mentioned in dispatches.

The first member of the AIF to get an accolade for performing a perfect wheelie.

What a bloody joke, he thought.

BUT New Guinea was no joke.

In fact everyone serving there with the AIF agreed it was a right bastard.

The second largest island in the world, New Guinea's southern-most tip was virtually on the same latitude as Australia's most northerly point, dangerously close to home to an invading force of fanatical Japanese.

The Japs had given Darwin a thorough blitzing. Although highly classified information, the Australian Government had drawn up emergency plans to abandon all but the south eastern corner of their continent to the anticipated invasion.

That would have meant Kerslake's cattle station getting a few Oriental visitors.

Not far short of panic, the Australian government recalled a complete division, including DR Rintzen, from North Africa, to be deployed to New Guinea.

Because the Japs had to capture New Guinea and particularly Port Moresby, its southernly situated capital, in order to be able to launch an amphibious assault.

So New Guinea was where they had to be stopped and the Aussies lost nearly 20,000 men doing so.

Jacko had considered the outback unforgiving territory but compared to New Guinea it was a holiday resort. No real roads or railways, a tangled morass of mangrove swamps, supply lines calf-deep mud through native tracks.

Rainfall could be 300 inches a year. Gnarled Aussie foot soldiers reckoned it rained for nine months, then the monsoon started.

If the weather didn't get you, the bugs did.

In temperatures in the mid-nineties with humidity to match, disease thrived. Malaria was the greatest threat, but delights like dengue fever, dysentery and scrub typhus were waiting too.

Because the terrain was impassable for a motorcyclist even as skilful as Jacko, being based in and around GHQ in Port Moresby avoided most of the bitter fighting with the Australian 5th and 7th Divisions around Lae, the Huon peninsula and in the malarious Bulolo Valley at Wau. His luck at dodging bullets seemed to have travelled from the desert to the jungle with him.

He stoically tolerated conditions because he'd discovered a new mission. He was determined to bring a little relief to the hundreds of mules and donkeys the armies utilised as the only form of transport capable of tackling the thick, soggy jungle trails.

Jacko thought the world of the mules. They were such gentle trusting creatures. Yet men with their wars had given them a life of absolute hardship, toil and almost certainly an agonising death.

Whenever he had the chance, Jacko spent time where the animals were tethered, mopping them down, trying to swab out and patch up their multiple sores and scabs, scrounging around for any old scraps to feed them.

The mules always recognised Jacko.

"I swear these buggers grin when they see you," reckoned one of the supply squaddies.

It was a poor elderly mule, staggering under a load, apparently on its last legs, which nearly brought Jacko's military downfall.

He had been sent twenty miles inland, with dispatches for an advanced column, up a winding track with steep gorges and chasm, choked with thick jungle with swampy carpets.

In near vertical rainfall, a mule train had been bogged down and Jacko had floored a sergeant who had been flailing the mule with a thick mangrove stalk. A perfect right hander.

"You better head back for base before this bastard has a chance to put you on a charge," advised one of the drenched infantryman.

With visibility hardly an arm's length, Jacko motored gently down the twisting trail, feeling very much the better for his unaccustomed aggression.

He was halfway back to Port Moresby when the burst of bullets hit him.

In the New Guinea jungle, there were isolated groups of Jap infantry swallowed up over vast stretches.

Jacko had ridden straight into disaster

Man and machine somersaulted off the track and tumbled down dozens of feet of thick mangrove. His natural reflexes, which had cushioned a number of speedway pile-ups, did not help.

He landed with a thwack in the slimy green. The bike ended several feet away. He had disappeared from sight. And he lost consciousness. Everything was black, black, black.

Jungle veterans insisted that a bloke could be swallowed up by the jungle, rot, and leave not a trace.

Nearly two days later, another bedraggled column splodging down the trail noticed what appeared to be a motor cycle poking out of the greenery, way below.

"If that's an Army bike, the rider must be down there somewhere," said the column leader. "Let's go down and take a squizzy. Can't leave the poor bleeder in an unmarked grave."

Thus Jacko was uncovered.

He was a shocking sight: covered with blood, bugs and bites.

But he was alive. Just. Only just.

CONSCIOUSNESS flickered painfully seventy-two hours later. It was a burning pain for Jacko to lift each eyelid. He wondered why he was in a cocoon on which someone had left a water tap running.

He was in a casualty aid station wrapped in mosquito net under a makeshift tarpaulin strung on struts, with monsoon rain battering down on it. Because his upper thigh and buttock injuries were so severe, he was lying facedown.

"So you're back with us," said a medic orderly in a gore-stained apron. "We thought you were with the angels more than once. Half your luck, mate."

Jacko's luck, a mystical quality which had become a speedway pits talking point after he walked away unscathed from track pile-ups, was still with him.

He had taken Japanese bullets in the hip, arm and head – plus one right up the jacksy as he somersaulted over the ravine.

Each had avoided a vital organ, although if the lead in the head had gone a fraction deeper his rescuers would have dug him a lonely jungle grave.

Jacko thought grimly he would have a few interesting scars to show his teammates in the dressing room. There was a joker at New Cross who had a six-inch livid stitched-up scar in his lumbar regions which a tattooist converted into a railway junction for him.

Lucky maybe. But Jacko's tough, monastic way of life had unquestionably been a key factor in staying alive.

He was gently moved on to the 2/7th General Military Hospital outside Port Moresby where the greatest concern for the medics was his raging fever. He had been bitten and stung repeatedly by a gruesome army of New Guinea's charming insect life. They had literally been eating him alive. Parts of his flesh were angry purple.

His blood count was a devil's brew of conflicting problems that even medics now experienced in tropical diseases could not isolate. He had swamp fever, malaria, multiple bullet wounds and a temperature simmering the thermometer at 105 degrees.

The medics were confident his injuries could be treated, would eventually heal. Except the malaria. A gentle giant of an Army doctor with a soft Tasmanian accent explained to Jacko that malaria was caused by a mosquito bite which was actually a blood-sucking action, leaving a parasite called a plasmodium which attacked the body's red blood cells.

And this little bastard of a parasite reproduces itself from time to time.

"Sounds encouraging," said Jacko, weakly. "Any good news?"

"Not to write home about," replied doc, kindly. "There are dozens of forms of malaria. The disease-bearing mozzies are the greatest killers of mankind. At least four of them are fatal, and one of the worst is a little shitbag called the plasmodium falcparium, which gets at the brain and kidneys causing a raging fever: shivering, splitting headaches, creaking joints, bit of delirium, lasting two or three days.

"That's the beauty who seems to have taken a liking to your life's blood and he's going to be in your system for the duration. We're dosing you with quinine which can keep it down but never rid you of the bastard. He will pop up and bop you at any time."

Jacko drifted for days, then weeks, in a half world, more dead than alive, shivering then burning, every joint aching, every movement agony.

He was barely able to be moved out of the isolation ward of the garrison hospital in Port Moresby. He lost all notion of time. He was floating in a shadowy world. He lost weight alarmingly.

But he became aware another patient had moved in with him. He was a half-mad medic called O'Reilly, thought to have cerebral malaria because he often screamed alarmingly in the night. At times he was a disconcerting ward mate. But he could be interesting and unusual company.

Once a Jesuit monk, he had been defrocked and disgraced for some dark reason. But was still full of riproaring fire and brimstone theories.

He knew he was dying but said: "Oh Jacko my boy, but I'm ready to meet my maker. I've spoken to him enough times he'll surely welcome me as a pal. Are you ready to meet your maker?"

"Dunno about that," croaked Jacko. "I've only really spoken to dogs and horses."

"Well now, there you go," replied O'Reilly, ever the theosophical thinker. "And who is to say that God isn't a horse or a dog? Sure isn't his name the same three letters as a dog?"

That was a thought that had never occurred to Jacko.

Recovering feebly from his death's door experience, he had plenty of time to mull it over.

DURING his lengthy recovery, Jacko had all the time in the world to turn his thoughts back to speedway racing, once the fever abated he started sitting up, taking solid foods without throwing up. He could consider the future again.

His old chum Bongo, learning that it could well be eighteen months recuperation for Jacko, mailed a bulging package of old speedway magazines and periodicals which Jacko greedily absorbed during endless days recovering strength.

It was then he read about, and became better acquainted with Max Octavius Grosskreutz.

Max was an archetypal Aussie dirt track pioneer, a former sugar cane cutter from Queensland and the only 'foreigner' in the Belle Vue (Manchester) side which had barnstormed most of the honours in British speedway during the Thirties.

Jacko learned that Max confessed to a dream, to build up his own superbike, which he vowed would be the fastest on two wheels. A dream machine. For some reason he christened it 'Pinto'. He worked on it through the night for weeks and kept it under wraps, refusing to divulge any of the secrets he had introduced into its development.

Workshop rumour insisted Maxie was using special light metals, personalised castings, revolutionary sprockets, countershafts and pistons.

When Pinto was finally ready to be tested, it promptly roared into a turn and threw Max on to his earhole with a bump.

Undismayed, Max insisted the machine had a mind of its own and that he would master it. Curiously it stirred memory pangs of dear old Bowz for Jacko. Finally, Max and Pinto merged as one and won most races by a straight. Together they were virtually unbeatable.

Rivals demanded to know Pinto's secret. They insisted the cubic capacity governing the legal power was measured but it proved to be within the 500c.c. limit. Other riders offered Max sizeable sums of money to borrow Pinto. He refused. "I'm the only bloke who will ride her," he insisted. "I'm not selling her secrets. I made that motor, and no-one will ride her except me."

But he made one exception. A very special exception. Robbed by injury of the chance to compete in the first official World Championship Final in 1936 Max agreed to loan his superbike Pinto to his fellow Australian Bluey Wilkinson for the Wembley-staged event.

He was unbeaten aboard her. But Pinto, the machine with a mind of its own, still had the last laugh.

Although the best man on the night, Wilkinson was not crowned the champion as he did not start with sufficient qualifying bonus points.

He was the only man ever to ride unbeaten in a World Final and not be crowned champion.

Because of Pinto…?

Jacko loved stories like these. He was thrilled to recall that Wilkinson had actually spoken to him, encouraged him. And that he had been present to witness inimitable Bluey winning the world crown two years later. They made him think, they provided aspiration, hope, inspiration to recover from his injuries.

Because he still had a dream.

If I can survive this little lot, I'm indestructible, he decided.

So as the Australian troops marched over the Owen Stanley Mountains and the beleaguered Japanese resorted to cannibalism, Jacko concentrated for hours, then days on how to improve his chances of reaching the pinnacle of world speedway.

He reached a few conclusions.

He would need two complete machines. He would build two Pintos.

He would always fit a new rear tyre for meetings.

He would find some analytical chemist who might have thoughts about doctoring race dope to make it more volatile. He knew some riders were dabbling with additives like ethyl, pictric acid, even iodine.

He calculated the lighter the machine, the quicker it would travel. Maybe only fractions. But they made the difference in the explosive action of four-lap oval track racing.

And reducing machine weight was a definite possibility. Lighten the frame, the forks, the handlebars. Hadn't he read about the blokes building ultra-lightweight stressed steel and riveted hulls for airships, a system called monocoque? Could that be used in speedway? What about titanium? That had only been around for a hundred and twenty five years but had anyone experimented with it in speedway?

Maybe he would lengthen his saddle to aid weight distribution. Tyres had to be regulation, but surely there was a method of deepening the tread to improve the grip?

Jacko decided to discuss his thoughts with Bongo. He wondered if he dare try to track down Grosskreutz, now a senior figure in Australian speedway, to discover if he'd mellowed in time and might reveal some of the secrets of his Pinto, his special bike. He would also make contact with Jim Chinnock. He grinned as he imagined Chinners' cocked head and derisive expression at his suggestions.

Jacko had been a natural on horseback and, in truth, had found competitive motorcycling a natural progression. It had always been fun. From now on, it must be ultra-professional.

And if I can find a little bit extra…Then the whole world can kiss my ass, thought Jacko.

He realised he was daydreaming

There was a long way to go.

His doctors were impressed by his progress but warned: "You've got the bug in your blood. Although we can stuff you with quinine it can return to flatten you at any time for the rest of your days."

He was unfit to continue military service and moved to a Recuperation Centre at Cairns, on the north Queensland coast.

While he was being disembarked his stretcher bearer took a look at his emaciated frame and deep sunken eyes and said: "PoW, were you, Dig? Dunno how you blokes survived."

Welcome home, Jacko.

CHAPTER 7

LANCE CORPORAL Stanley 'Dribbler' Prince stared miserably out through the high wire perimeter fence of Stalag XVI across a bleak Silesian landscape heavily hung with smog pregnant with the yellow fumes of the towering factories of Katowice away on the horizon.

Sod this for a game of soldiers, he thought. What a way to waste the best years of your life.

Compared to most of his wire-crazy chums, Stan was a short-term Kreigie: captured on the second day of the Anzio landings in Italy in January 1944. He had been sound asleep by the side of the road and awoken by four Bavarian farmboys in Panzer uniforms.

After humping and bumping about in the entrails of central Europe he had ended in a permanent camp in the direst region of southern Poland, near the Auschwitz concentration camp, about which very nasty rumours abounded.

Stan was a philosophical PoW.

While gaggles of gung-ho optimists plotted wild escapes, Stan settled to make the best of a grim existence.

Where would you head if you made it outside the wire?

Stalag XVI was around a thousand miles from what might be regarded as friendly territory. Stan spoke only English, with a distinct London North Circular twang, and he knew he had about as much chance of travelling unnoticed through enemy lines as an ostrich in an Arsenal football shirt.

Then it was either a quick bullet or a month in the cooler. Realistic Stan did not care for the odds. He was also claustrophobic about tunnelling. He settled for sitting out the duration.

And to consider how eventually he would inject a bit of spark into his life which, until now, had been pretty damned ordinary.

He was a suburban Londoner through and through. All his life had been spent as a resident of Crouch End, sprawled in the shade of Alexandra Palace, in one of thousands of dull, post-First World War semis, with regulation bay windows and coal fires. His mum had china ducks going up one wall.

Mum was an uncomplicated, unimaginative Londoner who had no inclination to move further than the end of her own street. She had to be dragged to the Empire Exhibition at the new-fangled Wembley complex.

Dad tried to be awfully respectable, working in the accounts department of a national newspaper in Fleet Street, a down-table pen pusher. He embarrassed Stan considerably by insisting on always wearing a bowler hat to the office. But he arranged an office boy job for Stan when he left school or, rather, lurched away.

Soccer had been Stan's greatest boyhood joy and obsession. His namesake Stan Matthews was his idol. How outraged he had been when Matthews and the rest of the England side had been ordered to give the Nazi salute to Adolf Hitler before playing in Berlin in the Thirties. How thrilled he had been when his idol tormented and ran rings around his German full back marker, steering England to a thumping 6-3 victory.

Like so many boys his age, he wanted to be like Stanley Matthews. So he wore baggy pants over incredibly bandy legs, played on the right wing, and tried to copy the famous Matthews ball dribbling technique.

On the recreation grounds and in the youth leagues of Crouch End and Colney Hatch he had built quite a reputation. So the nickname 'Dribbler' had been born. It remained with him when he joined up and in the carefree days of Army soccer.

His dad, puffed up with the importance of a position on a major newspaper, was racked with envy of the reporters' expenses that passed through his in-tray. And fancying himself as a creative writer he bought an upright Imperial typewriter and banged out what he considered to be purple prose, which attracted only dust until his wife quietly binned what he typed.

Skipping and skimping school homework, Stan had ample time and opportunity to teach himself to type and, in the hours when his dad was out of the house, he would sit hammering out his own special football reports.

He became quick and accurate and after a few months at work running messages down Carmelite Street and Fetter Lane, he drifted naturally up into the copytakers' pens in the editorial deptment. His willingness there was swiftly rewarded with a permanent position, mainly because he volunteered for the graveyard shifts, early in the morning, or through the night.

Stan spent uneventful years sat in a cubicle with a typewriter as big as the organ of the Odeon, Leicester Square, loaded with a carbon-backed double roll of copy paper like oversized toilet tissue, recording the reports from 'Short of Cirencester' and 'Brown of Shepton Mallet' and hundreds of nationwide editorial stringers.

He played football at every opportunity, courted a girl called Doreen who lived two streets away. They dated, danced together at football club functions, groped and fumbled down back alleys. And more or less agreed to be engaged.

Dorry had written to him in the PoW camp, promising she would wait. Laconic Stan had seen the suicidal anguish from so many 'Dear John' recipients in the camp too often. So, typically, he regarded the situation philosophically.

One of their regular pre-war dates had been Wembley Speedway on a Thursday evening. Harringay would have been nearer, but Wembley was special. Wembley was a cut above. If you supported the Lions you were superior to other track followers.

Stan's thoughts drifted pleasantly back to mild summer evenings, the sun setting on the North Circular Road, holding hands with Dorry way up between the Twin Towers, lapping up the exploits of Lionel Van Praag, and two of the Lions' emerging talents, Tommy Price and Australian Aub Lawson.

What a character, that Van Praag. Hadn't he once held up a bank with a toy pistol for a laugh? Or a bet? What a night it had been when he was crowned the first official World Champion in 1936. Didn't he hear Praagy was now one of the ace pilots in the RAAF?

Look at his life, what he's achieved, Stan thought. Then consider mine. It's farcical.

As a sooty dusk dripped down on Silesia, Stan the Dribbler decided that when he returned to civilisation he would do something, try anything, to inject meaningful razzle dazzle into his life. He mustn't end like his mum and dad.

Life is all about memories, he thought. It's up to me to make them good ones.

Maybe speedway racing would be the answer.

That thought sustained him through evening roll call.

Well, it was worth a go.

A bloke would go mad without his dreams in a PoW compound in the depths of tragic, war-torn Poland.

BORING hours drifted into weeks and months, with Lance Corporal Rintzen unfit for service so very gradually regaining his health, his only real interest and escape reading about speedway in the publications Bongo sent regularly.

Bongo did add that Kerslake had been asking about him and said to pass on the message that Jacko would be welcome back to the cattle station when he felt ready.

Jacko certainly wanted to return to straighten important matters out with Kerslake.

But he was increasingly obsessed with speedway. He wanted no other life. And the more he read, the more fascinated he became.

Sitting in the dappled afternoon sunlight of the hospital grounds, he greedily devoured the words of the man who had been so sympathetic to him during his distinctly unchequered pre-war speedway career, Old Foghorn at West Ham. He had been the man credited with staging the first speedway meeting.

As the newsvendors selling the evening papers outside Wimbledon Stadium used to cry, Jacko read all about it.

Foghorn had written:

"The date is November, 1923. It is the opening night of the speedway at West Maitland, Australia. There is a 'Grand Electric Light Carnival' with dancing on the green, and forty furious daredevils are going to race for the magnificent purse of £10.

"I was asked 'Say, what's the rules of this sport? How do we go?' I replied: First past the post wins, no putting a foot down at the bends. That's how she goes, Jimmy.

"Jimmy Datson and his brother Charlie; Tommy Benstead and Ernie Buck were among the youngsters who stripped their motors right there on the track, threw their jackets on the ground, rolled up their sleeves and waited for the gun.

"And what cycles they were! Big Harleys with turned up handlebars, Indians, Nortons, big Excelsiors; motor cycles of any horse power, any size. Eight men raced in each heat, all the races were handicaps.

"Safety fences in those days had never been heard of. Neither had jackets nor gauntlets. There was no loud speaker equipment. But this was sunny Australia in 1923 and speedway racing had yet to grow up.

"The noise of the open exhausts is deafening as the riders get on their marks and listen for the gun. Bang! The engines rev up and eight mechanically mounted men leap forward accompanied by the music of the Home Town brass band.

"Excitement among the spectators runs high; the screams of the women and the yippees of the cattle punchers can be heard even above the roar of the motors. The wild youth of the Hunter River Valley lean over the fence waving their stiff cardboard programmes in their excitement.

"The track is nearly a third of a mile long and the limit man has almost a lap start. The scratch man, No 86, is coming through the field. My oh my is that fellow travelling. It's the youngster Ernie Buck, of Dungag. He'll win – oh, curse. The electric lights are fading out. The man with the megaphone trying to explain to the crowd is shouted down.

"Lights flicker on again. The full moon looks out from behind a passing cloud. The race is restarted. Two men are disqualified for trailing their feet on the corners. Three motors fail to finish and the dance goes on over there by the poultry pavilion of the Agricultural Show.

"Falls? You're telling me. And spectators injured too. But who cares? We're through to the final with only five machines functioning and it's after eleven p.m.

"They're ready – and Jimmy Datson's motor won't start. Wait for him, wait for him. We wait. It's 11.30. The brass band has packed up long ago.

"They're off at last. Only one finisher. The others have fallen by the way. But speedway racing is born. A rush for horses, the galloping of stockmen on the back roads racing for home. Everybody excited, everybody happy."

Jacko could close his eyes and drift off to be there that historic day – in speedway folklore – at West Maitland. It reminded him so much of Baranga Showgrounds. He made a vow to make a pilgrimage to the birthplace of dirt tracking. He'd persuade Bongo to go with him. He realised guiltily that he wasn't even aware if speedway was still staged at the Hunter Valley centre.

Old Foghorn had headed the original party of Australian dirt trackers to Britain in 1928, on board the SS Oronsay. Jacko grinned to himself when he read Old Foghorn's reported dialogue of their initial experience of English racing conditions. It restoked memories of his own experiences at Wimbledon.

"Say, Foghorn, it's raining. They don't expect us to race in the rain, do they?

"Well, Ron. This is England. You and Charlie and Sig are in the headlines. You've nothing to beat. Rain or no rain, for goodness sake don't let these Pommies think you can't do what they can do."

There seemed a splendid symmetry about the British speedway situation when Jacko read that Old Foghorn was one of the first men to revive the sport at the end of the war.

True, Belle Vue (Manchester) had run afternoon meetings right through the war years. West Ham had staged a daylight meeting of sorts during the Phoney War.

But it was Old Foghorn who reopened post-war activity at Newcastle at Easter, 1945. And on June 23rd. in partnership with former Belle Vue star Eric Langton, introduced racing at Odsal Stadium, Bradford. Rascally Foghorn ran challenge matches with a Bradford side against various 'visitors', pretty well the same riders every week. But such was the euphoria that nobody cared.

Four days after the opening of Bradford, New Cross brought speedway back to London, with a series of individual meetings like the Victory Cup and London Riders Championship. Widely dispersed centres like Exeter, Glasgow (another Foghorn promotion), Sheffield and Middlesbrough swiftly set up shop.

With so many former riders like himself still tied up in the services, Jacko was fascinated to learn a typical week's racing diary for the handful of cinder-shifters around in 1945. It read: Saturday, Belle Vue (Manchester); Monday, Newcastle; Tuesday, Middlesbrough; Wednesday, Glasgow; Thursday, Exeter; Saturday afternoon, Bradford and Belle Vue on Saturday night.

Jacko was just itching to get back to racing.

His bullet wounds had healed satisfactorily. The medical orderlies had been impressed, bug-eyed, by the recovery of Jacko's up-the-jacksy damage. "Good God, man, you've got the toughest arse I've ever seen," retorted the resident MO on his rounds. "A hide like a rhinoceros. The bullets almost bounced off you." A lifetime in saddles of one description or another had its benefits, thought Jacko.

But time and again, just when Jacko felt he was on the move, the damnable plasmodium falciparium virus would bite anew and the fever would return.

It was going to be a long haul. But Jacko kept believing. His dream would one day be a reality.

One day.

BUT BEFORE he could contemplate his dream, Jacko had to face up to more homespun reality. He had to talk to Kerslake.

He had been away from the cattle station for over five years. Bongo picked up Jacko from the nearest railhead to Baranga, greeted him tearfully, trying not to show his dismay at his skeletal appearance. Jacko was still two stone below his old fighting weight, his demob suit hanging loosely.

The bunkhouse and yard had not changed, it was all hauntingly familiar to Jacko. Most of the hands were new, many of Jacko's pre-war contemporaries rested in war graves from Tobruk to Trinkamalee. Chazza had gone; Humpback was the new head hand.

Kerslake did not look a day older and still seemed to be wearing the same hat.

"Looks like you could do with a bloody good feed, boy," were his first words to Jacko.

For a couple of days, Jacko just drifted around, spent time with the horses, and a long, contemplative vigil under the eucalyptus where Blue rested in peace. The other, newer hands treated him respectfully, almost in awe.

"Reckon we need to have a talk," he said, at last confronting Kerslake.

"Yer, figure we do. Have a beer with me at sundown."

Jacko realised this was a mighty big moment. Kerslake had never been known to share his sundowner solitude.

They sat without speaking until Jacko said: "Couldn't help but notice how you were listed on my Army forms."

"Oh, yer."

"Why didn't you mention you had become by legal guardian? That you'd bloody adopted me."

A reflective minute before Kerslake growled: "Figured it wouldn't make much difference if you knew or not."

"But why bother? Life was okay for me as it was. I was getting by."

"I'll tell you why, boy" Jacko suddenly realised Kerslake was animated as rarely seen before. "Because our pox-ridden governments, not just content to rekky a bloke's best meat and horses to be slaughtered by the Johnny Turks, then have to stick their snotty noses into the way we handle our kids and our Aboriginals.

"Legislation, they called it. The right to take away orphans and shove them into a 'better life' in servitude with a bunch of Would-to-Godders. And they stole the Black Fellas' kids, bloody stole them, because they thought they knew best how to bring 'em up.

"I wasn't going going to let 'em get their hands on any of my station kids, not just for the sake of a signature on a bit of paper."

"Bit more than that, isn't it, sir. You were responsible for me."

"Well, I was anyway. Had been from the moment you first drew breath. Had to look after your Dad, too." Kerslake drank deeply of his beer.

Jacko reflected. "Can understand you looking after yer own. But you seem just as riled about the Black Fellas and their treatment."

"Jeez, that Army's made you a sneaky bugger, boy. Yer, I have my reasons. And nobody left on this station knows them. And I'm gonna tell you because, God help us, we're sort of related now. You gotta swear to keep it to yourself."

Taken completely aback, Jacko said: "Not a problem."

Kerslake topped up his tankard. "There's only ever been one woman in my life."

His eyes were fixed on the shimmering horizon. "I was just starting up the station, just about your age. She was truly beautiful. The only woman for me. Her name was Mali.

"She was an Aboriginal. Pure Australian. Her kind had been here for centuries before us immigrants arrived.

"Well, wouldn't you know the good folk of the community thought our relationship was contrary to God's wishes and told me she would have to move on. They said they had the bloody Government behind them.

"I said bollocks, that I wanted to make Mali my wife. Officially. You would have thought I'd threatened a seven year dengue fever.

"But the bastards won. While I was out on a drove, some so-called officials rode into the station and told all the Aboriginals to move on. Go long walkabouts. Or else. They knew what that meant. So do you, boy.

"Mali was ordered by her elders to move on with them. The Aboriginals always obey their elders. I rode bloody hundreds of miles looking for her. But those folk can disappear into thin air. Particularly if they're frightened of being lynched. Never did find her. And I must have spent a thousand nights sitting right here regretting it. And that I gave up looking for her.

"Never looked at another woman since.

"And I've taken every bloody opportunity to kick any so called official straight up the ass. And their shitty orders.

"So I sure as hell wasn't gonna allow some jumped-up little squirt to come and take one of my best drovers away. Telling me what to do with my own hands. You were too good a horseman to end up waiting table in some fancy homestead. I'd got used to having you around. So that's why I signed the form to make you sort of legal.

"Now I haven't chuntered on so much in twenty five years. Any other damn fool questions, boy?"

"Only one," said Jacko. "What's a Would-to-Godder?"

"Jeez, you must have bumped into all those self-righteous drongos who go through life saying 'would to God I could join the Army with you:, 'would to God you would see the evil in your ways.'

"Now, are you gonna return to your old job? Would to God you are," Kerslake was actually smiling.

"Well, not actually, sir," said Jacko. "I guess I'm in love with speedway the way you were with your Mali. I've got to go back to prove something to myself."

"In that case, I'll just shake your hand."

He also gave Jacko a bit of hug. It was a hitherto totally unknown display of

68

emotion. Jacko worried that he was going to say something apocalyptically embarrassing.

"Jeez, you're a boney bastard," said Kerslake.

CABLEGRAM FROM: Chinnock, Southampton Docks PO to Rintzel, Baranga cattle station:

YOUR IDEAS ARE NUTS STOP. DID THOSE BUGS GET INTO YOUR BRAIN STOP. BUT IF YOU BELIEVE, FAITH CAN MOVE MOUNTAINS STOP. SPEEDWAY HAS GONE MANIC HERE STOP. WHEN ARE YOU GOING TO COME TO FILL YOUR BOOTS STOP. LOVE CHINNERS.

Jacko had eventually tottered back to health. He moved from the cattle station into town, assisting the Drumma family business, enjoying working with saddles, making design refinements. He had learned a lot from Kerslake and discovered all his advice readily flooding back

Bongo was now running the saddlery and had opened a cold drinks emporium. He'd had an unremarkable war, never leaving Australia. He was making money fast, becoming far too fat and settled to consider riding again.

But he was 101 per cent behind Jacko's ambitions.

Although colourfully vilified by Kerslake, the Australian government passed some helpful legislation and, unlike their British counterparts, were particularly generous to servicemen returning from the war.

Those who were self-employed, as Jacko technically was, could apply for a £500 loan to set themselves up again. Anyone going into farming or agriculture could claim £1000. Jacko could have started his own cattle station. But there was only one way he was going to use the money.

To fulfil his speedway dreams.

So together Jacko and Bongo worked late into the steaming nights, building up two racing machines. Bongo stumped up extra cash without a quibble to import two of the latest JAP engines. Now weighing only fifty-seven pounds – Bongo had known heavier sewing machines – these developed 48 hp at 6500 rpm, the lowest pound weight per bhp developed in any unsupercharged engine on the world market.

Bongo liked the idea of a lightweight bike. He bored out the frame and forks, lightened and shortened the handlebars. In a moment of mischief, he even hollowed out the revolutionary new ballstop at the end of the clutch lever.

Jacko felt he could lift a machine with one hand.

They tested the machines at their old private training track at the back of the station. Jacko felt his strength and confidence surging back. The bikes went like a dream. He was gliding. It felt he was riding on a feather. Acceleration at the starts was little short of sensational. He rode in a couple of handicap events at Eldura Motordrome and picked off the front markers as though they were going backwards.

Watch out world, or at least England, here I come.

Then the bugs came back to haunt him. He was flattened by fever and accepted the 1947 British speedway season must be his logical target.

But Wimbledon seemed to have forgotten him. At the end of the war, the British track promoters had agreed to a rider pool to distribute equally all the available performers. Nobody had claimed Jacko. No surprise really. He wasn't in the country and the short word from Down Under insisted he was more dead than alive.

So Jacko was ready to turn back-somersaults when he was contacted by West Ham, the wonderful, charismatic East End arena which had miraculously survived the bombing when the Luftwaffe had plastered Docklands for seventy-six successive nights.

Although he had friends and many warm memories of Wimbledon (which had been bomb damaged, despite being in the relatively untargeted west side of London), Jacko secretly admitted to himself there was nowhere he would rather race than at Custom House, in the throbbing heart of Hammermania.

The new man in charge at West Ham was a rough diamond, a self-made second-hand car merchant from Essex, Vic Gordon.

A Hammer fan before the war, he had organised coaches every week for supporters from the Essex Estuary to attend meetings. He'd been a bouncer at Ilford Palais, packed a lethal hook with either fist, and had once knocked out cold a fan who dared to infiltrate the pits.

He had made a quick fortune when the second-hand car market boomed at the end of the war, had a liking for ostentatious motors and drove one of the very few Oldsmobile American limos in the United Kingdom.

Vic had been on the terraces when Jacko had done his blaze away for nothing party piece in 1938 and again the next year when he cleaned up (ridden unbeaten by an opponent) with more than a little help from Nipper Corbin.

He had not forgotten Jacko.

Vic was a tough nut but a no-nonsense operator.

"I'll fly you in," he told Jacko.

"Can I bring a bike, too?" Jacko asked.

"You'd better," came the answer. "It's bloody hard work running around."

So Jacko and one of his special featherweight bikes touched down after a three-day flight into a clutch of former RAF huts that passed for an airport at Northolt, West London.

Post-war England was about as cheerful as a February funeral in Siberia. The country was still gripped in one of the most brutal winters of the century. Temperatures were down to minus sixteen, there were twenty-feet snowdrifts. The Great North Road was blocked for twenty-two miles by ten-feet drifts. All shipping in the Channel was halted by blizzards. Widespread power cuts prevailed: Buckingham Palace, banks, law courts and departmental stores were working by candlelight.

The food situation was desperate with virtual starvation rationing; butchers sold out of fresh meat, corned beef only (twopence-worth a week), shops limiting potato sales to two pounds per head.

Extreme shortages of eggs, fish, butter and sugar. Food queues hundreds of yards long twelve hours a day.

Forget about fruit, biscuits or chocolate bars. Absolutely no chance. You were more likely to obtain moon rock than a banana. The pubs ran out of beer. There was no appreciable heating. Newspapers were restricted to four pages.

After six years of bombs, doodlebugs, sleeping in shelters and London Underground stations, shutdown theatres and stadia, Britain's exhausted population were entertainment-starved too.

Cinemas, the opiate of the people, although attracting millions weekly, closed, through lack of heating and power to run the projectors. People sat crouched, shivering over old steam radios, even listening raptly to programmes like Sandy Macpherson on a funereal organ, Dick Barton Special Agent (for kids) and Woman's Hour (even the men). Folk listened to programmes of community whistling.

London was still startlingly bomb damaged. Jacko thought: England won the war. What must Germany look like?

The only upbeat angle seemed to be that speedway racing was restarting after its winter break.

The first-post war season, 1946, had surely been the sensation of the nation. Capacity crowds crammed into London's stadia. After a six-year closure in a season from the end of March until early October, over 6,500,000 fans clicked through the turnstiles of British tracks. The total was 2,500,000 more than 1938, the previous best year, over £1 million poured into speedway's coffers.

On three occasions Empire Stadium, Wembley, packed in a crowd exceeding

80,000. The official Wembley Lions Supporters Club had 60,00 registered members. Before the all-ticket British Riders Championship Final at Empire Stadium, an ordinary league match between the Lions and West Ham had attracted 80,000. Even in pouring rain in October, 85,000 crammed into Wembley, with a further 20,000 locked out listening to the progress of the meeting through the stadium loudspeakers. Wembley's car park recorded over 2000 vehicles, more than the FA Cup Final, at a time when there was a chronic shortage both of vehicles and petrol.

West Ham had been erupting each Tuesday with over 40,000-60,000 fans every week. At the final Wimbledon meeting of the season, 30,000 were squeezed in while police grappled with gate-crashers outside. And this was no Cup Final. It was a friendly match between the Dons and Wembley. They were being turned away at New Cross and Belle Vue (which had actually staged a few wartime meetings having satisfied the authorities that the bikes were not using fuel from the war effort). The Manchester track had a crowd of 40,000 as late as November for the National Trophy final against Wimbledon. House full notices were everywhere.

Old Foghorn, ever the optimistic wandering entrepreneur, had started speedway at the gigantic bowl of Odsal Stadium, home to the Bradford Northern Rugby League club.

Speedway riders were frantically feted folk heroes, mobbed like movie stars, earning fabulous sums, hundreds of pounds a week when the average worker was pleased to take home a fiver. Speedway was king. Jacko had flown back into the whambam, wildfire phenomenon of the Forties.

TO HIS CONSIDERABLE surprise, Stan Prince discovered Dorry still waiting for him when he was eventually repatriated and arrived back in Crouch End with his accumulated backpay burning a hole in the pocket of his floppy demob suit.

She also seemed to have acquired a fair slice of sexual experience locked away night after night in air raid shelters and dodging incoming V2 rockets. "Well, we had to do something to take our mind off the bombs," she said.

Stan was pulled swiftly into her bed while her mum was listening to Variety Bandbox on the BBC Light Programme downstairs. He was slightly overwhelmed but grateful. He had been a celibate PoW for a long time. She also talked about marriage.

Not well received were Stan's carefully nurtured notions about trying to cheer up his peacetime existence learning to be a speedway rider.

Like most of her contemporaries, Dorry still attended Wembley Speedway – she was one of the 60,000 registered members of the official Supporters Club. It required five full-sized riverboats for a club outing on the Thames. Dorry admitted she fancied half the Wembley team. She was a different girl from the one Stan had known before the war.

She insisted his back pay should go towards their wedding. She was not amused her fiancé should risk his neck on short track cinders racing. She certainly did not want her beloved exposed to the predatory females she witnessed regularly hanging around the pits, dressing rooms and car parks. She had overheard their conversations in the Ladies.

But Stan insisted: "I promised myself when I was stuck in the Stalag I would do something to liven up my life after the war. I can make twice the money at speedway than I can working shifts in Fleet Street. I'll double up on shifts and still get time off to ride.

"I want to make enough money to get a place of our own instead of having to rely on your mum."

Dorry was hooked on the idea of a place of her own so she compromised: "If you're not showing a profit out of speedway in twelve months then you jack it in and concentrate on a proper job."

So Stan enrolled in the beginners' class at the only academy for London's speedways, the tricky Rye House track on the banks of the River Lea at Hoddesdon, Hertfordshire, where Londoners like to spend lazy summer Sunday afternoons.

For a fiver a man could hire a bike, leathers, boots, get practice laps and instruction from a gnarled prewar Australian dirt track racing veteran who liked to sit in his office picking a crab to pieces, noisily sucking the pincers.

"Done any speedway before?" he asked Stan. "Motor cycling?"

"I was pretty handy on a Royal Enfield before the war," replied Stan.

After tentative, exploratory laps, Stan became handy on a speedway bike, scooting the machine around the inside white line, using minimum throttle, avoiding the riproaring fence bashing of his fellow pupils.

One of those fellows had played prewar soccer against Stan and still called him Dribbler.

The Crab-Crunching Instructor snorted and remarked: "Not a bad name for him on speedway, either. He dribbles around the inside all the time. He's certainly no throttle-crazy cinders shifter."

Stan persevered. Weekend after weekend, he clocked up the practice laps. Always careful. Never impetuous.

As a soccer player he had developed a good sense of balance. He was fit, lived frugally; the PoW experience had hardened him. Mechanically, he was a quick learner. As a kid he could strip and rebuild a typewriter. He knew what made his old Royal Enfield tick. In the Army he had been adept at stripping Brens and Sten submachine-carbines. He avidly studied the JAP speedway engine. It helped that the engine had been developed by J.A. Prestwich in a North London workshop two miles from Stan's front door.

At every opportunity he sniffed around at JAP's, learning about engines, hearing about new concepts and prototypes. The JAP management, impressed by Stan's enthusiasm, allowed him to build up his own machine from odd spares and parts. His efforts became the work's pet project. All the workshop mechanics contributed.

After several weeks' work, Stan had infinitely superior equipment to all his fellow trainees at Rye House. He was virtually a works-sponsored rider.

"You're not a master mechanic, Stan," said the top JAP executive. "But you're a damned good tinkerer."

At the end of the term, with autumn approaching, Rye House staged their annual nursery championship. On his immaculately tinkered machinery, Stan steered clear of the track acrobatics of his classmates to finish second overall. His prize: a pair of fur-lined racing boots. Would have been handier in the Stalag, thought Stan.

All the major London clubs kept an eye on the emerging talent at Rye House. Wembley manager Alec Johnson, who had a Tudor home in Hertfordshire, was a regular visitor, having signed up more than one useful graduate. He was respected in speedway for his 'eye for talent'.

He quietly watched the nursery championship from a corner of the pits, absorbed by Stan's controlled performance. His Wembley did not really suit full-throttle fence scrapers.

To the Crab Cruncher he said: "That Stan bloke is clever. He only does enough. I might give him a go against my juniors."

"You won't have to pay much travelling money," replied the instructor. "He lives right on top of Wembley Stadium and he's so darned careful he'll probably run down the hill to you without starting his car."

Of course, Stan leapt at the chance to appear in a second half Lions Cub Scramble at Empire Stadium. Bright-eyed hopefuls simply did not turn down Wembley.

Stan would be earning something out of speedway well inside Dorry's deadline. He would need the money. Dorry was pregnant.

Unreal. Stan felt like a little boy who had accidentally walked on to a film set when he was allowed entrance through the Pits Gate at Wembley for the first time.

He was handed a Wembley Lions body colour to wear. He was billed as Stanley in the programme, which briefly described him as a local boy who had caught the eye of the boss at the Rye House training circuit. Several fans gave him the thumbs up. He recognised and talked to a couple of fellows he'd played soccer against.

Dorry was permitted to sit in the rider's wives enclosure. She was fretting but happy not to have to pay an admittance fee. Waiting for his second half opportunity, Stan watched seated on the greyhound track wall, a little overawed by the atmosphere and the near presence of riders who had been his heroes for years.

The racing seemed spectacularly faster from this angle than spectating 40 rows up.

His first race against fellow juniors was a splendid farce. It lasted 40 yards. Everyone fell. Stan did not actually hit the track. He scuffed to a halt as the others spread-eagled around him.

'Restart with all four riders,' said the announcer. 'Our second half junior events are never dull, are they folks?'

In the rerun, Stan moved intuitively to the inside, hugging the white line. His machinery, tidied up by JAP workshop staff, was considerably quicker than his junior rivals.

He tootled – relatively untroubled – to a slowish win. A similarly uneventful performance in his second outing brought a second place. Total earnings £7, more than he would earn in a week battering out copy about dockyard unrest from Giles of Gosport.

The Speedway Gazette reported: 'Wembley seem to have come up with another useful discovery from their Rye House production line in Stan Prince. He isn't a natural thrillmaker but he's effective and technically appears sound. One to watch for the future'.

But as Britain's first post-war season unfolded, with hysteria and attendances reaching unprecedented levels, Stan had to settle for once a week second half opportunities at Wembley. He earned a few extra quid. He was not driven restlessly by ambition. He had other responsibilities to consider.

Dorry and Stan married, rather quietly and in rather a hurry. Many couples did in those bewildering post-war days.

A parsimonious pair, they had sufficient funds for a reception at The Minstrel Boy, Colney Hatch. Wembley Lions Supporters Club sent a telegram of congratulations. Wembley boss Alex Johnson dropped in to toast the happy couple.

'I've been having thoughts about what to do with you next season,' he confided, interestlingly, to Stan.

The newly-weds honeymooned at the Cliffs Pavilion, Southend, leaving Stan drained. He then moved in with Dorry's Mum in Crouch End. Her ear was consistently glued to the BBC Light Programme.

Stan had an unexpected first request at his new address. 'I'll have to keep my JAP engine in the airing cupboard during the winter to keep it warm,' he insisted.

CHAPTER 8

ENGLAND was a world apart from the land Jacko Rintzen had left six years earlier, but there were wonderfully familiar grinning faces to greet him.

Nipper and Chinners.

Happy-go-lucky, cheeky Nipper was a changed character. He never got to be a fighter pilot, having to settle for six years as an aircraft fitter. He had a few squeakers when London's airfields were targeted during the Battle of Britain. His mum had been killed in a bombing raid on Southampton.

Speedway's authorities had decided there were not sufficient overseas riders to restart the World Championship, so the British Riders Championship, although including Australians, became the big night, the sport's Blue Riband. Ralph Greenhalgh pleaded for his return to Wimbledon for the 1946 season. Nipper's great all-round ability had taken him to the runners-up position in the British Riders Championship Final. But Nipper said he'd retired although still only in his twenties. Like Vic Gordon he had made a mint from the second-hand car market on the South Coast – and he'd fallen in love with golf.

He explained: "Never had a bad accident, see, moosh. I got thinking that one night some loonyhead is going to run me through the fence. I started to be obsessed that speedway had a real bad bang waiting for me. I'm not like you. You bounce. Reckoned I'd get out before speedway got me."

He was destined to be one of the greatest riders never to have won the world championship.

Nipper had married a lovely, warm smiling girl called Anne and bought an impressive house on the water at Hamble, Hampshire. Nipper liked to smell the salt of the sea.

He insisted there was ample room for Jacko to stay with him for the duration. He could hardly go back to the Wimbledon kennels. Poor Ruthie had been fatally hit by a V1 rocket while queuing for dog scraps. Her skill as a seamstress was gone forever. Jacko vowed to himself that he would never part with the neck scarf she had embroidered for him. Doll had found a bloke who had shagged her and not sodded off and lived in an apartment block in Tooting.

Chinners looked like he spent all the Second World War sleeping in the same overalls. His tremendous mechanical ability had propelled him to the rank of colour-sergeant in the Royal Electrical and Mechanical Engineers.

He regarded Jacko's new equipment thoughtfully.

"Run on iodine, does it?" he inquired. "You'll be able to clean out your wounds from the fuel tank if you fall off."

But when he lifted, stripped, then started the engine in the workshop, Chinners nodded grimly. "Might have something here, Jacko," he grudgingly admitted.

With Nipper now retired, Chinners agreed to work for Jacko "to see how it goes".

Vic Gordon provided a Ford pickup for transport; West Ham would deduct a fiver a week from his pay cheque to cover the cost. Ordinary team members were making at least seventy-five pounds a week; Nipper had cleared three thousand for his one post-war season.

Jacko was ready to rumble.

SOMEHOW it was appropriate that his first meeting back in Britain was an away fixture at booming Bradford, Old Foghorn's wildly successful new enterprise. The dear old boy had figured so much in pivotal moments of Jacko's English adventure so far.

"Good to see you again, son," he growled. "You were my greatest ever gift to old Greenhalgh at Wimbledon. But don't you go making a mug out of my Boomers tonight."

In the wonderfully offbeat manner of speedway team nicknames, the Odsal outfit were known as the Boomerangs, the historic Australian hardwood missile.

Surveying the drab West Yorkshire industrial centre, Jacko thought it could hardly be less like the environment where you would find a boomerang. Grey, smoggy, a sea of smoke stacks, and like pretty well every town and hamlet showing ugly scars of war damage.

Odsal Stadium was gaunt. But awesome. Only a rickety stand and not much covered accommodation. But set in a natural bowl, it had steepling terraces, with around 300 steps to the top. From the dressing room above the terracing to the pits on the first corner was like descending Ayers Rock.

Dressing room scuttlebutt – and wasn't it great to be back among the irreverent crowd – insisted that Old Foghorn was in such a panic to cash in on the post-war entertainment gold rush that he didn't lay a track with proper foundations. He had simply thrown a few thousand tons of factory waste (of which there was an abundance in Bradford) around the outside of the pitch – and at the bottom steps of the terraces!

The track was, he was warned, rough as old boots.

Jacko picked up all the wicked ruts in his first ride back in Britain, bucked and jumped but held on. His balance and control were still exquisite. Sheer power propelled him into second place.

Bongo's workmanship and inspiration seemed to have given him an extra gear. He simply flew out of the starts. Even Chinners was impressed. Other riders in the pits eagerly sniffed around his machine. "Just like they did to Max Grosskreutz," mused Jacko. Eleven points in his first meeting as a Hammer. He had earned over thirty pounds.

Barney Stacey, best-known of the vividly colourful speedway correspondents at least two generations ahead of their time in Fleet Street wrote:

West Ham's airlift gamble on Jacko Rintzen has hit pure Aussie gold. He is the new Thunder From Down Under.

Not until Jacko emerged for his first home meeting at West Ham did he encounter the frenzied hysteria that hallmarked Britain's first post-war fan mania.

As he walked into the main arena from the dressing room under the main stand to go to the pits on the apex of the first and second corners, over 40,000 fans erupted in a howl of welcome.

Then three wild-eyed girls dodged the security men, dashed across the centre green to bowl him over, screaming and apparently trying to rip his leathers off. Pandemonium. And much ribald ribbing when he was eventually escorted to safe harbour in the pits.

"You'll learn to sneak around the back way," said bossman Vic. "Those female predators will tear you to pieces."

After the war, an experimental new silver sand top surface had replaced the cinders at West Ham. It suited Jacko sensationally, quite literally down to the ground.

He reeled off four straight wins, the machine virtually running away with him up to the first corner. Riding a middle and outside line, the first advice from his learner days, he simply vanished over the horizon up front. He was blazing away and all his rivals were getting burned.

He fought his way through hundreds of fans in the carpark back to the pick-up, signed endless autographs (including one on a sheet of toilet paper). The windscreen of the pick-up was covered in lipstick messages. There were knickers stuffed in the exhaust pipe.

It was a mad, mad world.

But Jacko found he was loving every moment.

AS THE HARSHEST of winters melted into one of the most glorious sunny summers in living memory, the days became steadily more golden for Jacko.

With his wiry, whiplash physique and razor reactions, he was the perfect shape for a speedway rider. He was as lean and mean as a lonesome polecat.

With Chinners breathing beautifully on his machinery, his motors hardly missed a beat. His mechanic had kept his prewar machine under wraps for years, spruced it for Jacko to have as a spare.

It seemed a bit of a beast when pressed into action, but Jacko still won races aboard it.

"All in the mind, Jacko," said Chinners. "Question of confidence."

West Ham Speedway was the non-stop talk of the East End, the track Hammers greater heroes than cavalier cricketer Denis Compton, who hit 3,816 runs and eighteen centuries during the heatwave summer, or heavyweight boxer Bruce Woodcock, who had been hoping to challenge for Joe Louis's world title.

West Ham's footballers, operating across the Barking Road at Upton Park, were not considered in the same breath. Frank Sinatra would have been ignored in E13.

Jacko wallowed in the camaraderie of his charismatic team-mates. His captain was an elegant Canadian with a clipped moustache and a fine bass baritone voice, who often accepted engagements to sing with a pianist to refined Palm Court gatherings.

He had another chum who had been a prisoner of the Japs, survived the Death Railway and one of the A-bombs and still picked his teeth with barbed wire.

Jacko bonded particularly well with a genuine gor blimey East End boy called Ben Silva, who had graduated, like Nipper, via bombsite cycle speedway. He would wander the dressing room stark naked, playing a banjo he called his 'plonker' and singing Maybe Its Because I'm A Londoner, one of the hit songs of 1947.

The West Ham Supporters Club, thriving with 25,000 fanatical members, were aghast that Jacko had his own leathers embossed with the red and yellow colours of deadly rivals Wimbledon. They presented him with another immaculately tailored set, with epaulettes in the red, blue and white of West Ham. But he still always wore Ruthie's scarf.

Bossman Gordon worked feverishly fanning the phenomenon. He was a publicity junkie. Jacko became the 'Outback Rocket', 'The Kid From Nowhere' and was mobbed whenever he appeared. Not just at the track. He was even besieged for autographs in public toilets.

The West Ham boss loved Jacko because he fitted exactly into his theories of 'image'.

"Speedway riders should be like Hollywood movie stars," said Vic. "Unattainable. Unattached. Glamorous.

"It makes me spew when I see riders rolling up for meetings in a family saloon, with the wife and two kids and a bloody spaniel on the back seat. If that image grows we'll soon all be back in the soup queues.

"Stay available, Jacko. The one thing Hitler got right was keeping his women out of sight and convincing all the people that he was married to the nation."

Yeah, but look how Hitler – and his last-minute wife – ended up, thought Jacko.

He could hardly avoid female attention. Female fans everywhere literally threw themselves at him. Vic Gordon allotted two massive minders in white coats called Ted and Fred to protect him at all London meetings. Unlike many of his racing contemporaries, Jacko, always uncomfortable and aware of his gaucherie in female company, did not respond enthusiastically to the attention.

There was, as they said, plenty of it about. Jacko was amazed at the outrageous behaviour. He signed autographs on stomachs, breasts and buttocks. He had his first experience of a lovebite, which caused much merriment in the communal dressing room bath. "Bitten by the bloodsucker of Barkingside," said Ben Silva. It all rather frightened Jacko. He dreaded being caught in the act in his own wagon, in some council flat, or humping on Hackney Marshes.

And he hadn't his own home to go to for discretion. He was far too considerate a lodger to drag some screaming scrubber back to Nipper's Hamble residence.

So as austerity and rationing worsened in the sunshine, milk allowance cut to two pints a week, the Labour Government was forced to pass legislation to control 'spivs and drones on the streets'.

Jacko concentrated on speedway.

He experienced Wembley from the racing angle. It was not a disappointment, even if Sir Arthur Elvin, MBE, (he had been honoured on June 13th 1946) programmed him as Jon Rintzel. The 70,000 crowd seemed to suck him a foot in the air. The track, although sited outside the soccer pitch and inside the greyhound track, was a really good racer. The starting gate was not halfway up the home straight; it was a shorter dash to the first turn, which suited Jacko's swift getaways.

The first two turns were sharpish, the pit corner more sweeping. They needed a different approach. There was a long run-in to the line. Wembley was supposed to be a trick track, with a pronounced advantage for the home riders. A Wembley rider had won the Riders Championship Final there in 1946 and the Lions had won the league title. They were the dominant force in '47.

But Jacko felt he could enjoy racing at this magnificent monolith. He had a feeling of destiny there.

For the first time in his career, he faced hostility, audience abuse. Returning to Wimbledon as the star of a rival London outfit, he was subjected to a raucous reception and a sea of placards scrawled 'Judas', 'Dirty Turncoat', even one saying 'Jacko – Speedway's Lord Haw Haw' (the notorious Nazi propagandist who was executed for treason).

Ralph Greenhalgh in his programme notes described him as "the best terrace sweeper we've had".

But a bright-eyed little lad, seeking an autograph through the railings protecting the pits, piped: "We still love you really, Jacko."

The reception didn't seem so bad after that.

SO PERILOUSLY CLOSE to death so recently, Jacko decided that life could surely be no better than his summer of '47.

Blazing temperatures meant slicker, smoother tracks which suited his style. Racing four, sometimes five times weekly in the white-hot hysteria of British post-war speedway, he could not recall missing one start.

He normally outgated everyone, even the crafty old veterans adept at rolling or split-second tape-raising anticipation.

If he was not clear at the first turn he was 'in with the boys' at the corner and well positioned to pounce, change line and accelerate to the front. Nobody left Jacko stranded at the back at the starts.

Rick Eldon, widely respected speedway correspondent and editor of the Speedway Echo, called him: The Fastest Alive Over The First 25.

His motors simply seemed to run away with him. One or two suspicious oldtimers, who had things much their own way immediately after the war, claimed they were illegal, big 'uns, more than 500 cc. They were formally measured and found to be legal, to great snorts of derision from Jim Chinnock. Occasionally during the summer he felt fatigued, a little shivery, but there was far too much going on to worry.

Prize money seemed to arrive by the bucketload. Some track bosses slipped him wads of appearance money in buff envelopes. He was in demand, big box office.

Accolades and national recognition too.

He appeared on the front cover of the mass circulation Picture Post with the banner: The Kid From Nowhere Is The Toast of London.

He sat a photo session for speedway's ace cameraman, the garrulous, but talented Wilf Eden, which ended up splashed all over Britain's three weekly speedway magazines. Imaginative Eden had arranged to hire a couple of kangaroos for the session. Jacko had seen a million before but never actually stroked one on the nose. The joeys seemed much taken by him, and posed for the camera like old pros.

He was asked for a photo sit with one of the pin-up starlets from Gainsborough Studios who was making a movie called 'A Boy, A Girl and A Bike' Somebody said her name was Diana Dors. She was an impressive young lady. Jacko thought the boys back on the station would have been much taken by her.

International recognition, too. His sensational form was recognised by the Australian Test Match selectors, first at reserve, then in the team proper. The Aussies lost all three Tests, at Bradford, West Ham, and Wembley but agreed that Jacko's development had been their major bonus of the series.

Surprisingly, news of his international call-up even reached Baranga.

The cable read:

DAMN YOU AND YOUR SPEEDWAY STOP. ALL MY HANDS WANT TO BE RIDERS NOW STOP. VERY PROUD OF YOU. GREG KERSLAKE.

First time I've ever seen the old bugger's Christian name, thought Jacko. But he basked warmly within at Kerslake's words.

As the sizzling summer mellowed into autumn, influential Barney Stacey wrote:

Boom year! In spite of austerity and all that goes to make a restriction-fettered, war-

weary land, speedway racing went roaring to town in 1947.

But speedway's boom year must go down in the history books as Jacko's year. Virtually unknown prewar, almost mortally wounded in the war, with his distinctive peaked helmet and flowing white neck scarf, he made an impact as no other rider has ever done before.

He rode undefeated for West Ham through 15 of 24 league matches, dropping only 16 points all season. He breathed new life and fire into the test series and is one of the favourites to win the season's climax event, the British Riders Championship final at Wembley.

So great has the Jacko reputation become that the fans have almost wearied of cheering his victories but scream hysterically when he's beaten. No greater tribute can be paid to the man's progress.

Just that big night at Wembley to complete the fairystory.

But even as Northern fans were climbing aboard their coaches for the long haul to North London, Jacko awoke to the dreaded symptoms of his jungle ordeal: leaden eyelids, agonised joints, quaking shivering fits, high fever. Malaria. The docs had warned the wicked falciparium strain would never go completely.

Vic Gordon telephoned the Speedway Control Board in Pall Mall and said: "Impossible for Rintzel to ride at Wembley. He's willing to try but he's too weak to hang on to a bike for five yards, never mind five races in a Championship Final. He is too valuable for West Ham to risk."

Reporting for the Daily Express, Barney Stacey wrote:

Ninety thousand fans hailed Britain's new speedway king but it was the man who wasn't there everyone was talking about.

Without Jacko Rintzen, a victim of the deadly malaria mosquitoes, the Final was like Hamlet without the Prince of Denmark. But even the Bard of Avon would never have dreamed a plot like this championship final.

An Aussie beaten by a mozzy.

CHAPTER 9

WHEN THE ARCTIC WINTER weather eased and weary-looking green shoots finally poked their heads up in the London suburbs, Stan Prince returned to Rye House to prepare for the 1947 season.

Advance bookings for practice laps were essential as hundreds, thousands, of young men seeking post-war adventure, tried to get aboard the speedway bandwagon.

It was the get-rich-quick, South Sea Bubble sensation of the moment.

Influential Wembley booked regular weekend practice periods for their riders to stretch their muscles, try out equipment, shake off winter cobwebs.

Boss Johnson buttonholed Stan on the first weekend. "I'm giving you a junior contract," he said, greatly brightening Stan's day. "You'll get regular rides at Wembley. But you need experience of proper league racing. I think you should go out on loan to a lower league club."

So explosive had been the boom in post-war speedway that an entirely new, eight-club Third Division was to operate in the sport's second post-war season.

Stan was farmed out to the new Eastbourne Eagles. On his first sighting of his new home he realised farmed was an appropriate term. The track was set in meadowland, down a cart track off the A22 at Hailsham, six miles London side of Eastbourne, the Sussex seaside town more recognised for bath chairs than broadsiding bikes.

The track had no covered accommodation, parts of the safety fence were old bedsteads, the management heated the water in the tumbledown dressing sheds by lighting a log fire under the tank. There was a well in the middle of the centre green. The track owner, a likeable ex-rider making a fortune in post-war redevelopment, practised his golfing chips into the well before meetings.

Certainly not Wembley, thought Stan.

But Eastbourne had character, spirit and a wonderful sense of fun. And Stan's tidy style suited the Eastbourne track, an evenly balanced 342-yarder. It looked like a small track, but you attacked it like a big one. It was a good place to learn.

He quickly became a track specialist. All the new clubs were staffed almost exclusively with newcomers to speedway, like Stan, with limited experience particularly away from their home circuits.

Home meetings became rather a pension for Stan. Although Third Division pay rates were only thirty per cent of those in senior racing, averaging ten points weekly at Eastbourne produced a pay cheque for Stan more than double the average weekly working wage.

He grew to love the knockabout, carefree atmosphere of Third Division racing.

With a newly-acquired 1938 Ford Eight – one of the senior Wembley stars had a car sales business in the Edgware Road and gave him a special deal – Stan ventured forth adventurously on away trips to places he'd hardly heard of.

He went west to Exeter, a massive 440-yard steeply banked town centre track with thirty-two-feet wide bends which you rode like a wall of death. Stan did not care much for it. Then on down to Plymouth, the town still Blitz-ravaged, and another cow-pasture raceway.

Stan learned that when you went west you stayed overnight at a rambling guest house at Haldon, where the landlady and her two buxom daughters, known as The Sexeter Sisters, were speedway-crazy and did not charge for erotic extras. There was a very well-known apple-cheeked, generously proportioned girl fan at Plymouth called Cornish Patsy, too.

Stan had learned about the Track Spare Code around the speedways. It applied wholeheartedly throughout all the divisions.

Officially, a Track Spare was a speedway machine, maintained by club managements by club mechanics, for the free use of team riders having problems with their own machinery during official fixtures.

But 'Track Spares' was also the saucy sobriquet for the free and easy, headhunting speedway camp followers at every circuit. Around West Ham they had names like Glenys the Menace from Goodmayes, Yo-Yo Knickers of the East India Dock Road, and Doormat Dora of Dagenham, so called because she had pubes like the Matto Grosso. At Eastbourne Stan was aware of the Brighton Ballbuster and the Hellingly Angel. The predatory girls maintained a curious but strict code of behaviour.

Neither riders nor ravers ever talked about, or worse still gloated over, their erotic but mostly snatched experiences. It was a kind of *omerta*.

Stan was careful to play strictly away from home. Dorry kept a beady eye on him. But he was usually too wrapped up in racing to contemplate physical pleasures.

He was two hours driving blindly around the streets of outer Birmingham before he stumbled into Cradley Heath, buried deep in the Black Country, famed only for the manufacture of manhole covers, a warm-hearted lady caterer who specialised in black pudding sandwiches – and its speedway team.

Tamworth, further east across the Midlands, was set in grounds between a stately home and a pig farm. Wombwell was almost buried by slagheaps in Yorkshire colliery country. They had no problems obtaining cinder top surface. Most of the faces on the gritty terraces were coal-smeared.

A major kick when Stan visited Stoke, managing to watch his boyhood idol Stan Matthews in live action for the first time. Soccer was still special for Stan. At least now he had walked on Wembley's hallowed turf.

Southampton was the most glamorous of the Third Division ugly ducklings. The Saints had been a senior force before the war, but for some dark reason had been instructed by the Speedway Control Board to work their way back up through the system, starting at the bottom. Their pretty little Banister Court track, festooned with fairylights strung between the floodlights, was a joy to ride. You loosened up, literally, by visiting the ice rink which was part of the complex.

Although a completely different world from the grandeur of the major London stadia, Third Division racing was booming. Somehow the crowds, tightly packed on open terracing, created an intimate atmosphere of their own.

Stan emerged as one of the new stars of the section, winning his first piece of silver when Eastbourne sneaked in at the post to win the league championship in the last week of the season, after the staging of the British Riders Championship at Wembley.

It was the hot chat of speedway that Jacko Rintzen, who had been flying all season, had been robbed of the title by malaria, of all things.

And I thought it was tough with a running cold and diarrhoea in Silesia, thought Stan.

CHAPTER 10

EVERY DAY when she went to the office in London's Olympic year of 1948, Anne 'Fan' Harris thought she could not escape from Jacko Rintzen.

A massive billboard at Upton Park District Line Underground Station was emblazoned: Whacko, Jacko's Backo – Every Tuesday at West Ham Speedway 7.45 pm. A huge image of a rider wearing a breastplate body colour of blue and red, with dominant white crossed Hammers. He had nice eyes but needed to do something about his hair.

There was another at all the ten stops along the line to Liverpool Street, then on the three Central Line stations to Chancery Lane, where she alighted for the office where she worked in Theobalds Road.

Rintzen was plastered all over the East End from Canning Town to Chigwell. West Ham Speedway boss Vic Gordon knew how to cash in on a whizbang box office sensation.

Anne was an East End girl born and bred but not a typical one. She arrived in the year of the Depression, as speedway racing was starting at West Ham Stadium.

When she started talking she could not get her tongue around her name but managed to mouth 'Fan'. Everyone had called her that through toddlerhood, schooldays and now in the office.

Her father Reg had been chief fire officer at East Ham, a dedicated, disciplined type, always immaculate in his appearance. As a girl, Fan had considered him the most handsome man in the world. She was at an impressionable age when he perished in one of the first air raids of the Blitz, trapped in a blazing Dockland warehouse.

She subsequently lived with her mother Diana, who had always completely overwhelmed, overpowered and outshone her. At Butlins, Clacton, the year before, Fan had won the holiday princess title but Diana won more rapturous applause as mum of the week and seduced the head Redcoat.

From girlhood Fan's mother had been determined to get out of the East End and find something better.

She was a considerable beauty, a child of the Charleston Age, a devotee of the early days of the movies and a sucker for a man in a uniform. She even fancied the Beefeaters at the Tower of London.

Somebody had told her she looked like Mary Pickford, so she became a bottle blonde. She was obsessed by a glamorous, silver screen image; never a hair out of place, always immaculately dressed and made up. She created her own distinctive black beauty spot on one cheek, imitating Margaret Lockwood, the pin-up darling of British films at the time.

Fan would shake her head in disbelief as her mum applied night make-up and wore the sheerest, most revealing lingerie every bedtime. Diana had read that most Hollywood sirens and grand titled English ladies hated body hair so, at some discomfort, totally depilated. Must keep up appearances, darling.

They lived together above a modest florists in Green Street, E17, just along the way from Upton Park, West Ham United FC headquarters. It was hardly Hollywood Boulevard.

Reg Harris, well organised and abstemious, had left a few hundred pounds and a reasonable pension, sufficient to support the little flower shop which had been in Diana's family for a couple of generations. It had been boarded up during the war. Not much call for bouquets during the Blitz – and Diana was superstitious about funeral flowers. But with Britain desperately trying to brighten up, post-war business was picking up.

Besides, men came from miles around to chat up Diana. With her trim figure, dazzling silver hair and crisp white overalls, she was the Belle of the Boleyn. Diana never had any trouble obtaining nylon stockings. Every spiv for square miles nurtured notions of banging down the door of her boudoir.

She certainly had a way with the fellows. She avidly consumed tales of the Babylon years of Hollywood and was fascinated by the scandalous secrets being whispered about Wallis Simpson, the American divorcee who had brought about the Abdication. Hadn't she visited the darkest dens of the Orient to learn erotic tricks that would drive a man to distraction? That's what newspapers insisted.

What a right result Mrs Simpson had achieved. She snared the bloody king. And didn't he look sensational in that naval uniform with all the gold braid. Diana had nothing but admiration.

The merriest of widows, Diana believed the Wallis way with men was the winning format: tease them, taunt them, then behave like the wildest whore and leave them drained.

Growing up in the shadow of her ravishing mum, Fan could not help but feel insignificant, insecure. Yet she emerged from torrid teenage years of Morrison air raid shelters, gasmasks and wartime rationing with poise and a quiet, bewitching smile.

She did not realise she was a very pretty girl: dark hair, by no means typical East End mousy, always neat, clean, tied back. Like so many war kids, she had impressive level teeth and her mother's complexion (without needing make-up), hazel-flecked eyes shaped like almonds.

An athlete's slender physique, she had been a useful high hurdler at school. She was a feline female, keenly chatted up by a succession of boring boys with awful Brylcreemed hair. They all seemed to get on better with her mum.

Fan had been above average at school, impressive considering her age group had missed much of the curriculum through the bombing. With quiet dedication she became very swift and accurate at Pitman's shorthand and timed at sixty words per minute on a big old upright Underwood typewriter.

Like her mother, she was absolutely determined to shake grotty Green Street right out of her hair.

At least as a competent shorthand/typist she could get as far away as the City of London every day. Which brought her into daily contact with Jacko Rintzen on the District Line.

Fan worked for a dusty firm of lawyers adjoining Lincoln's Inn, and soon became highly regarded, and fancied, by all the drips in their high collars and pin stripes, particularly an ex-Winchester public schoolboy called Andrew – everyone in the office pronounced it 'Ayn-droo'. His family lived on the Isle of Wight and seemed loaded.

She hesitantly accepted his invitation for a lunchtime drink at The Mitre in Hatton Garden, then an outing to The Wig & Pen Club on the border of The Strand and Fleet Street, a haunt of the legal profession since the Great Fire of London. He introduced her to white wine. He was different from the budding wide boys who groped her outside the Ilford Palais. His family were into yachting. He had a Swallow-class craft on the Solent.

"Come down for the weekend," he said. "You'll absolutely adore it."

Well, it's even further away from Green Street, thought Fan, accepting with a fleeting flash of her perfect teeth.

It was a different world and they were different people and after a morning in the fresh sea air Fan, in white short sleeved blouse and white shorts showing off her good hurdler's legs turned every head as she and Andrew walked into a pub called The Bugle at Hamble for a drink and hope there might be a sandwich on offer.

Sitting alone at a window seat, an oddly familiar face.

After a couple of moments consideration, Fan walked across to him and said: "You're Jacko."

SUNDAY was truly a day of rest in 1948 Britain. You either went to church or listened to a droning male voice choir on Family Favourites on the BBC Light Programme before the pubs opened for a grudging two hours at noon.

Nipper played golf every Sunday morning so Jacko, relaxed at being away from the frenzy of London speedway and attention of crazy girl fans, strolled down alone to Nipper's local, The Bugle at Hamble, to watch idly as the little boats drifted by.

A vision of loveliness with great teeth and terrific legs cocked an eyebrow at him and said: "You're Jacko."

"Yes, hello," he smiled shyly. "Do you want me to sign something?"

"Not really, thank you," said The Vision. "I just wanted to be sure that you're the one on that West Ham Speedway advert."

"Do you know West Ham Speedway?" asked Jacko.

There was not one soul living east of Tower Bridge who did not know West Ham Speedway.

"I live about a mile and a half away," said Fan. "My mum went once and reckoned she was a week washing the cinders out of her hair."

"That must be the reason mine is always all over the place," said Jacko. He really did have nice eyes, but seemed ill at ease talking to her.

Andrew hovered impatiently so Fan said: "Got to go. Sorry to trouble you."

"It's a real pleasure," replied Jacko.

Fan returned to Green Street to find Diana sprawled on the sofa in a silk dressing gown, reading Forever Amber and listening to a string quartet on the wireless.

She had spent two hours practising applying lipstick to look like Deanna Durbin. Sunday was that sort of day in 1948.

"I'm going to West Ham Speedway on Tuesday," Fan said.

"You must be mad," replied Diana. "It will ruin your hair and you will be half crushed to death."

But Fan was determined to see this painfully shy guy in action at his place of work and what all the ballyhoo was about.

Diana had her own car, a Standard Eight, which she drove rather badly. She had seduced a dealer in Seven Kings, left him gasping for breath but promising her a car at a giveaway price. She drove Fan down Green Street, across the Barking Road then ran into gridlocked traffic for the last mile around West Ham Stadium.

"You'll have to fight your way through on foot the rest of the way," she told Fan. "And make your own way home. Oh, and wear a headscarf."

Fan was virtually carried by the thronging crowd into the stadium precinct, joined a fifty-yard, four-deep queue at the first turnstile available, paid her shilling and ninepence admittance, then literally barged her way on to the terraces.

When she could force a passage no further, she looked across the arena. She was jammed into fans on the fourth corner, looking down the home straight behind the starting gate. The pits were at the opposite end, at the apex of the first two corners.

"Is it possible to get down near the pits?" she asked a Hammer-festooned girl wedged in at her side. "Only if you wanna fight your way through for a fortnight," the girl replied. "Once you're in here, darling, you can't move a foot in any direction."

The atmosphere was feverish, the noise like approaching thunder from 45,000 fanatics as the track staff, military in their red and blue jerseys with crossed Hammers and jaunty berets, marched onto the centre green, the tannoy blaring Blaze Away.

Jacko was in heat three. The first two races went by in a whirligig of noise, flying dirt and what Fan considered to be incomprehensible mayhem. She did not understand a word the track announcer said or what was happening.

When Jacko emerged from the pits, right at the other end of the arena, Fan thought how he looked neater, somehow more graceful, than the earlier leather-clad gladiators.

A crescendo of noise. Jacko, Jacko, Jacko – the chant echoed around the terraces. Jacko, Jacko, champ-ion, champ-ion. She saw a huge banner had been unfurled along almost the length of the tiered main stand which read: Our Jacko Is The Real British Champion. What could it all mean?

Tightly packed fans to her left on the third turn, bedecked in red and yellow, spat abuse and derision as Jacko cruised to the starting line. Inexplicably, they were chanting "Mozz-ee, mozz-ee," The Hammers were at home to Wimbledon.

He was on the outside starting grid, wearing a red helmet with a broad peak, in polished black leathers, his Hammers body colour with a huge white 3 on the back, a flowing white neck scarf. Fan thought it was unfair he had to start on the outside. Surely it would be further for him to travel around the first turns than the riders on the inside? As a schoolgirl hurdler, Fan was used to staggered starts over 440 yards, with the outside lane being favoured.

She caught her breath as the revs of four 500 cc machines reached maximum, the starting tapes flew up and men and machines threw themselves at the first corner. From her vantage position behind the start, she could not judge who was in front but as the four men broadsided then straightened up, she gasped as the slender figure in the red helmet swooped around the outside, roared down the back straight his scarf flowing in the slipstream, went impossibly sideways again seemingly coming right at her on the third turn.

He flew past her corner, right out on the safety fence, in front and glancing repeatedly to his inside, looking for team partner Ben Silva. Fan was hit squarely by a faceful of dirt before the pair soared shoulder to shoulder over the finish line after lap one.

Fan looked around as Jacko steered his local boy partner to a maximum heat win. It was as though all the girls near her were at a religious meeting. They were repeating Jacko, Jacko, Jacko. It was an incantation, a prayer. One girl, almost in tears, clutched rosary beads.

Fan had to admit Jacko looked a different class. He was dashing. He seemed to fly away from the starts. He looked in control, part of the bike. Other riders seemed to be fighting their machines. Jacko seemed to caress his.

She had to admit this speedway business was more circus than sport. She started to understand why millions of fans found it such an exhilarating escape from the drudgery of post-war Britain.

Jacko was top scoring Hammer again as West Ham easily defeated Wimbledon. A contented glow seemed to radiate down the terraces. The winning team paraded, squashed together in the back of a pick-up that hauled the track grader between heats. Eruption again around the terraces as the fans showed their appreciation, showering the grader with cigarettes, chocolate, fruit, luxury goods, almost unobtainable at the time. I'm Forever Blowing Bubbles echoed around Docklands.

Fan glimpsed Jacko's strawy thatch as the grader went past the fourth turn. He was waving shyly, almost apologetically to the crowd. Now there actually were girls sobbing. It was Fan's first experience of Hammermania.

"Well, what did you think?" asked her mum, after she arrived back home approaching midnight, having shoved her way out of the stadium and through the crowded streets.

"I can honestly say I've never seen anything like it," said Fan.

"Your hair's an absolute mess," said Diana.

CHAPTER 11

DRIVER Ritchie Mackay initially heard and smelled speedway racing from inside a bare cell in the Army prison at Bielefeld, BAOR.

"What's all the carry on?" he asked the provost sergeant.

"It's your Service Corps mates trying to be speedway riders," replied the guard. "They all want to be wealthy bigtime stars when they get back home."

Ritchie had heard only vaguely about this speedway racing, staged at White City, a fifteen-minute tramcar ride across from his home in Glasgow.

"Is there money in it, then," he asked.

"Sacks of it," came the reply. "They say there are blokes riding on cinders back home earning as much as film stars. It's the latest sensation."

Any angle involving cash attracted Ritchie's attention. For as far back as he could remember, finding and hanging on to money had been a losing battle for him.

Tenement-born and raised during the Depression years in Glasgow, with continual marches, strikes and industrial unrest in the shipyards and dockyards, Ritchie had to grow up street-wise, with a sharp sense of survival.

His father had laboured in John Brown's shipyards all his working life, escaping the monotony only on a Saturday afternoon at Firhill watching Partick Thistle lose and for a couple of hours afterwards moaning with his cronies about their performance over a couple of drams in Gregor's Bar.

Ritchie was still running the streets and raking the middens when he decided he wanted a little more out of life than his father.

On being ejected from school, he bucked the straight-into-the shipyards system, starting work as a trainee waiter at the LMS Hotel, overhanging Glasgow Central station. Fifteen bob a week, and as many tips as he could fiddle. He also had to help with washing dishes, but at least he was not wearing a flat cap and hobnail boots every day.

He learned quickly that ladies in dining parties responded to attention, so played up to them shamelessly, attracting many a discreetly slipped bob or two as he delivered their fur-collared coats and sweeping brimmed hats.

He also learned resentment. Some diners treated him like dirt, called him boy, snapped their fingers. Grand ladies contemptuously regarded him as barely human. "Just you remember your place," the head waiter growled at him. "No ideas above your station, boy. You're just a menial."

As he grew older, Ritchie's bitterness flowered aggressively. The privileged few lived in almost total affluence and leisure. So many, like him, had one foot in the gutter all their life.

The hopelessly repressive social system projected wild fantasies. One day he would be good enough for these wealthy folk. One day he would have these haughty beautiful perfumed ladies on their knees, begging for his attention.

Like most of the ragged street-running kids around Glasgow's tenements, Ritchie had been an early starter in sexual experience. But it was all gropey, fumbling, uncomfortable coitus with frizzy-haired girls in baggy knickers, often no knickers at all. On cobbles, or backlots, sometimes even in graveyards.

It was pleasurable but snatched. Ritchie knew it could surely be so much better. He watched films with Hollywood movie queens in boudoirs dripping in lace. His imagination ran crazy at the thought of a bunk-up in a bed. He was fed up grazing his knees. So he dreamed about fragrant ladies with elegantly manicured finger nails who wore silken dressing gowns, and what he would do to them.

He was smart enough to know he couldn't beat the privileged classes.

He would have to join them.

FIRST STEP on the ladder came with the chance to work, and live in, at Gleneagles Golf Course, waiting in the club restaurant, still aware of the affluence and lifestyle of the members he was serving. With his willing cheerfulness, he did all right out of them. He even earned threepenny bits risking life and limb retrieving shanked golf balls which had landed on the main railway line adjoining the fifteenth fairway.

Again, lady members in their crisp blouses and eye shades appeared utterly beyond reach.

But, thought Ritchie mischievously, nobody can stop me thinking about it.

He even took his wicked thoughts into the Army. He found himself with fanciful thoughts about a WRAC captain who looked just like Princess Elizabeth

Too young for active service during the Second World War, Ritchie had still been called up right at the end of hostilities. He wormed his way into the Service Corps because he thought it would be useful to learn how to drive. The chauffeurs lounging around in the Gleneagles car park seemed to have a cushier life than blokes serving steak and kidney pie. They were frequently on their own with very lovely ladies, too.

He had been posted to Bielefeld, the courts martial centre, and, after a few months, found himself utilising their facilities, standing at attention before a judge advocate having been caught selling off siphoned military petrol to a gang of German wideboys.

One hundred and twelve days, everything at the double, and only the noise and peculiar smell of stripped-down service motor cycles to distract his thoughts.

In an imaginative moment, someone at ENSA had arranged a visit from a party of immediate post-war British speedway riders to entertain the troops on improvised circuits around the Rhineland.

A riotous success, it had encouraged every squaddie with the slightest mechanical inclination to try to emulate these dashing characters of the speedways. They were broadsiding, tentatively but with abounding enthusiasm, outside Ritchie's cell.

On his release from the glasshouse, Ritchie, always with a sharp eye for the main chance, found himself in the same Nissen hut as two of the would-be track stars.

In the next bed, 'Slider' Smith, who had completed his driver's trade course with Ritchie, was convinced he was all set for the life of Riley, having arranged for a trial with his nearest club, Newcastle, on demob.

"I'll be making a hundred quid a week," he told Ritchie. "And there's women ten deep around every speedway pits, gasping for it."

Ritchie, a far better driver than Slider, thought: "A hundred a week and unlimited legovers. I'll have a bit of that. If Slider can do it, so can I."

GOOD DRIVERS had little problem finding work in post-war Glasgow, busily

clearing up after lengthy attention from the Luftwaffe.

Ritchie handled a two-ton tiploader for a demolition contractor, earned regular money, developed a liking for a pint with a dram chaser with his dad and discovered a couple of recently demobbed types like himself who thought speedway racing might inject a bit of glamour into a potentially humdrum existence.

They went together to White City Stadium at Ibrox, not far from Glasgow Rangers HQ. It was the home of the Glasgow Tigers in the Northern League of British speedway. Ritchie's first impression: yes, there are a lot of women about. They seemed to be completely crackers about the riders.

An article in the programme revealed that the training track at Bothwell, outside Glasgow, was now open, attracting dozens of would-be speedway stars. One of the most promising was an ex-Army racer called Slider Smith from nearby Newcastle.

The following weekend, Ritchie quietly drove his truck the twenty miles to the training centre and was reunited with his BAOR hutmate.

"Ay up, Ritchie, thought you'd be shacked up with some rich widow by now," was Slider's greeting.

"Just a matter of time," said Ritchie. "What do I do to have a blast at this carry-on?"

He was booked in for tuition, discovering his classmates were exclusively Scots like him – apart from Slider, who was not categorised as a beginner.

"Speedway has been going in Scotland since 1930," explained a wrinkly ex-rider turned instructor called Joe Lowther. "But Scotland has never produced a really good rider. Reckon all the local lads are fed up with the lassies throwing themselves at the Sassenachs and Aussies in the Tigers team."

So Ritchie became a member of Bothwell trainees, dubbed the Clydeside Sliders by the boss of the Tigers, the son of a famous dirt track pioneer who was constantly seeking the crowd-pulling potential of a genuine local boy for the Glasgow side.

In a matter of weeks, Ritchie was emerging as the lad most likely.

On track, he was the steadiest of all the trainees and had been able to acquire his own JAP equipment when his millionaire demolition contractor boss, who fancied himself as a sporting philanderer, had paid the bills.

When the Tigers boss believed he was ready for a junior outing at White City, he asked him a few questions for an introductory piece in the programme.

"What do you hope to achieve out of speedway?" he asked.

Retorted Ritchie: "To be famous enough to marry Princess Elizabeth. It's high time we had a Scottish king on the English throne."

With a warm glow, the Tigers chief thought: "I like this boy's style. He looks a typical Scot, square-jawed, gingery haired, full of sauce and aggression. He could be a racing Rob Roy."

ROCKET FUEL. Jacko was lost in thought about juicing up his racing dope as he gazed across the water during his usual Sunday morning routine at The Bugle, Hampshire.

There was a daft Aussie over at Harringay experimenting with what he called rocket fuel, similar to that used by Nazi doodlebugs. Might be something in it.

Mind, the same Aussie had blown up his workshop and destroyed half the drains in Melbourne. He was also legendary in dressing rooms for his ability to light a fart. Jacko smiled inwardly at the memory. He loved all the dressing room nonsense.

Then that vision of loveliness from the Sunday before materialised, perfect teeth, and poise you didn't often see in post-war Britain.

"Hello, I actually went to West Ham Speedway on Tuesday," she said. "You were very good. You seemed to be much faster than anyone else."

"I've got the best mechanic," replied Jacko. "It's all down to him."

"Have you always been a motorcycle man?" she asked.

"Nope, bikes have been a sort of escape, really. I'm really a horse man. They're my greatest love. Dogs, too. Most animals."

What an unusual boy, thought Fan. An animal nut. Most of the boys she had met behaved like nutty animals.

It seemed somehow natural to pull up a chair. Jacko discovered he was pleased she had.

"What about your fella?' he asked.

"Oh, he's involved in some regatta all afternoon," she replied. "He's got some old school chum who is going to be sailing for Britain in the Olympics in the summer. And he's not my fella."

To his considerable surprise, Jacko found he was pleased about that.

She was easy to talk to. Jacko had never before felt so comfortable in female company. They talked about her job, and where she lived with her Mum and Dad. A coincidence that Jacko's Dad had perished the same way, by fire. She listened to his description of Baranga. It sounded like a different planet.

He didn't talk about speedway. Although when she told him her name was Ann but everyone called her Fan he said: "You must be the only one who doesn't want my autograph."

She inquired why some of the people at West Ham had been shouting "mozz-ee" at him.

He explained quietly about how malaria had ruled him out of the previous year's Riders Championship Final. He didn't say how he had picked up the bug. Fan assumed it must be common in the Australian outback.

As lunchtime closing time approached, she realised she did not want to part company.

"Tell you what," she said, her eyes bright. "Do you realise there are herds of wild horses in The New Forest, not half an hour's drive from here?"

Wild horses in England? Jacko was dubious, but impressed.

"If you have petrol coupons, I could show them to you," she said.

Jacko had no problems with petrol. The Main Bar at West Ham Stadium on speedway and greyhound nights was packed with coupon-dealing, pencilled-moustached East End spivs, involved in more business than the Stock Exchange.

They drove together in Jacko's pick-up, out over the bridge at Southampton Water, down through Cadnam onto the A35 and, only two dozen yards down a leafy turnoff they found a group of New Forest ponies, grazing free as they had since the days of William the Conqueror.

Jacko was incredulous and pulled off the road. Getting out, he and Fan walked towards them.

Then Fan realised something very strange was happening. The ponies, normally wild and wary of humans, drifted towards Jacko, and allowed him to knuckle the back of their necks. He seemed to be whispering to them. Intriguingly, he appeared to be carressing their upper lips, sending the animals into an almost hypnotic trance. Quite amazing. But, when she approached, they stirred skittishly until Jacko talked to them again.

This boy appeared to have magic with animals. Christ, if only those screaming fans can could see them now, thought Fan.

They walked to a cottage serving tea – rationing ruled out any chance of food. It seemed natural to hold hands. They strolled deeper into the forest and, as if on cue, across a clearing three fallow deer gambolled, frisky but graceful.

"Oh, it's just like a film set," said Fan, finding herself actually hugging Jacko. She and her Mum had been to the cinema to see Walt Disney's blockbuster Bambi and she had wept copiously, but she had never seen a live deer.

Jacko could not recall a better day in his life. It seemed natural to be talking to this vibrant, stunning girl.

When they parted at Hamble, Fan brushed his lips with a kiss and said: "Shall we do it again next weekend? I'll try and get some time off and come down on the train."

Jacko wanted that more than anything he could remember.

CHAPTER 12

UNTIL last weekend, thought Jacko, I was living like Dick Barton, Special Agent – the BBC, in a most spectacularly prim mood, had made headlines by issuing guidelines to the scriptwriters of the nightly radio serial insisting: "Sex plays no part in his adventures."

But now Jacko actually had a date with a rare beauty.

West Ham had to travel north to Belle Vue (Manchester) the night before, but that wasn't going to stop Jacko.

He drove up the A5 alone, while Chinners agreed to ferry his bikes and return them to the workshops.

Jacko went through the old Nipper Belle Vue routine on the Big Dipper then went to greet the amusement park elephant. It was a new one: the old jumbo had died during the war. Jacko wondered what you did with a dead elephant.

It was the expected rough and tumble out on the track. Jacko picked up ten points cleanly then dashed to drive through the night back to Hamble.

He thought Fan looked like a million quid. Could this girl actually be waiting for him?

They drove even deeper into the New Forest, discovered ponies would eat out of your hand, and actually stumbled across wild pigs rooting about. They walked and laughed and held hands and discovered a hidden-away tavern in a village called Rufus Stone, which served supper of sorts. Neither was aware of time. Fan had arranged the Monday and Tuesday off so Jacko suggested he run her back to town when he went up for his home match with the Hammers.

"I'll get you into the directors' box," he said. "You won't have to worry about your hair there."

They talked non-stop, most of it nonsense. Jacko had never been so relaxed. Fan looked at an inscription on the pub wall and learned the village was named after King William II, son of William the Conquerer, who was killed nearby, hit by an arrow while hunting deer. He was called Rufus because he had a ruddy complexion.

"He must have had a bloody black heart too, killing deer," said Jacko.

The pub had a piano and a few locals were gathered around singing On A Slow Boat To China, the hit of the year. Certainly more romantic than the raucous pub singsongs than Jacko recalled with Ruthie and Doll in the White Lion, Plough Lane. Dear Ruthie and Doll. Whatever would they think about him having a smashing girl like Fan Harris all to himself?

Neither wanted the day to end. Fan knew she would have to make the decisive move.

"I'll go to see if they can fix us with a room," she said.

He awoke as morning sunshine filtered through the bottle-glass windows, felt the sensual warmth of slumbering Fan still snuggled up to him and thought: last year I honestly thought life could not get any better. Now I realise I didn't know I was born.

Fan was more experienced than Jacko but not that much. Jacko had been used to women behaving like hogs on heat, but Fan had been gentle and guiding, responsive and tender, passionate and a tantilising touch trashy. She was her mother's daughter in bed.

It was as though both had been saving themselves for this soft spring night in the heart of an English forest.

Jacko was absolutely certain that this girl was the only one for him. There could be no others. This was the edge of the ultimate human experience.

They had talked for hours in the darkness, content to be close.

Jacko communicated with her as he had with no other human being. He told her about Bowz and Blue and Kerslake. Good God, thought Fan to herself. Even Walt Disney couldn't dream up this sort of drama. He whispered quietly about his agony, how he had turned to speedway to escape from his memories. And how it had worked so well. But how his horse and dog still haunted him. There was never a day they didn't cross his mind. He had never shared these thoughts with any living soul.

Fan bit her lip as she ran her fingers lightly over the patchwork of scars on Jacko's naked body, testimony of Nipponese marksmanship in New Guinea. How desperately close to death Jacko had been. And if he had died she would not have met this remarkable man.

"The scars are nothing," he said. "Never talk about them. It's the hidden wounds that are the real bastards."

"But you could be dead," whispered Fan.

"Yeah, but I had a crazy religious nut next to me in field hospital who said we all go when our time comes, whatever. Reckon he's right."

Caressing him delicately, Fan was aware of the hard, tensile, physical strength of this sensitive human being lying close to her. Broadish, shoulders, yet tapering hips, wrists and forearms like stressed steel, sinewy horseman's legs, not a spare ounce anywhere. Fan had slept with two boys before Jacko. One had worn a vest with sleeves down to his elbows. The other had a protuberant ribcage. Most boys of her age, due mainly to the war, were seven-stone weaklings. Jacko was a different sort of man altogether. He was delicious. She wanted to keep him forever. She wanted to mother him, smother him.

Fan was surprisingly well read. Travelling the Underground for two hours each day, she waded through literature. Unlike her mum – or maybe because of her mum – she shunned the romantics. She consumed Wodehouse, C.S. Forrester and Ernest Hemingway. She preferred authors with style and flair. Curious – Hemingway had a cat with the name "Boice", almost the same as Jacko's horse. She thought of Hemingway, giggled throatily, and said: "Jacko, you've got the physique of a bullfighter, a matador. You know about bullfighting in Spain, don't you?"

"Sure, reckon it would be a fairer fight if the blokes went into the ring without a sword," he replied. "Blood sports are a disgrace. They should be stopped."

"But people reckon speedway is a blood sport," mused Fan. "Riders are killed all the time. Lots of people go just to see you crash. What about your crashes?"

"I bounce. I fall pretty," he said, his teeth showing in the darkness. "At least, that is what the rest of the blokes say. I know the risks. I control my own destiny. The poor old bull hasn't a chance. I've worked with bulls and respect them.

He added, grinning: "You know, in one day they can get around and keep an awful lot of cows happy."

"You're not a bull," said Fan, beaming. "Just you keep me happy."

HE WAS by no means a happy man, but West Ham supremo Vic Gordon made arrangements for Fan to be a directors' box guest – on a few conditions.

He had recently attracted back-page banner headlines in two London evening newspapers revealing Jacko had a 'no-marriage' clause written into his contract. The last thing he needed was his star attraction being seen with a girl in tow. An East End secretary, at that.

"Has she got a friend, or better still a granny she can bring?" Vic asked Jacko. "I don't want her to be seen alone with you."

"She's got her mum," replied Jacko. In their intimate, post-coital conversations, Fan had told Jacko about her madcap, mantrap mum.

"I'll get them a taxi and admittance to the directors' enclosure. You can sneak down and meet them in the boardroom at the end of the meeting. You do nothing, leave the details to me."

Fan burst breezily back home and said to Diana: "We've both been invited to the directors' box at West Ham Speedway tonight. Don't worry, you won't get dirt in your hair or spoil your make-up."

Diana was aware her daughter had been liaising with this rider whose image was plastered all over the East End. Mother and daughter confided all their secrets. She looked quizzically at Fan, so alive and happy, and said: "You've been with him, haven't you?"

"Oh mum, I'm crazy about him. You'll adore him, I know, I just know."

Diana sighed hugely. "My God, girl, I hope you know what you're doing. Every dirt track rider I've heard about for the past twenty years has horns and cloven hooves."

But secretly she was impressed by an invitation to the directors' box. West Ham Speedway was the biggest deal in a twenty-mile radius. There were bound to be plenty of interesting, well-off men in there on race night. And she was desperate to meet this wonderman who seemed to have captured her pretty, clever daughter's heart. Her daughter's previous boyfriends had hardly captured her attention.

When the pair entered the exclusive enclosure, high in the main stand, level with the starting gate, it was Diana, eye-catching in a little grey mink stole (she had bought from the whipround collection when her fireman husband died) who looked most like a glamorous visiting celebrity. She made an entrance like royalty. Laidback Fan was more like her hand maiden.

Fan had a completely different impression of the sheer panoramic energy of the arena from on high than when crammed among the raving female fans on the fourth turn.

Her stupid heart was pounding when she absorbed thousands of Jacko placards in a crazy pattern spilling down the packed terraces. 'I'm like a lovesick twelve-year-old' she thought.

When Jacko came on parade, flanked by his two minders, to a riot of noise, Diana grabbed her arm and whispered urgently: "My God, darling. He's gorgeous. He looks like one of those knights from the age of chivalry, going to joust for a maiden's favours."

From her new lofty viewpoint, Fan marvelled anew at Jacko's grace and mastery. His starting seemed yards quicker than anyone. He swooped on an outside line, spraying dirt, his motor screaming as he flew down the straights, his trademark scarf billowing out behind.

She discovered her breath gagging in her throat in one race when there was a multiple pile-up on the first corner, as all four riders aimed for the same line of track. A machine somersaulted spectacularly over the fence onto the greyhound track. Only one rider escaped the melee of men and machines. He had been a vital yard clear on the outside. Fan just knew it would be Jacko.

Sure enough, when the red stop-race light flashed on, Jacko was easing up down the back straight, casually looking back over his left shoulder at the carnage.

He stopped to give his partner a lift back to the pits on the rear of his saddle. A torrent of applause for his gesture.

Once again Fan's agile mind thought: this is theatre. No wonder thousands of fans prefer this to the BBC Light Programme and Music While You Work.

Diana was right into her riproaring Belle of Boleyn routine. She smiled dazzlingly at a couple of visiting pressmen and collared the track doctor to talk about her PMT. She disappeared into the main bar for a couple of races where she chatted animatedly with at least half a dozen spiv-type characters who were grinning weasily. She seemed an old friend of the West Ham Stadium company secretary in his winged collars.

"Used to supply him with button holes," she whispered.

Nobody paid much attention to Fan. She preferred it that way. She was entranced, in a thrall. The London post-war speedway bug had bitten and converted a cynic.

After racing, they were shown down to the the oak-panelled boardroom, deep in the main stand, with its massive antique table and private bar, with a white jacketed waiter in attendance.

On the wall behind the chairman's seat, a huge picture of the Blitz, taken by a Luftwaffe cameraman, with bombers over Dockland and West Ham Stadium clearly visible below in the centre of all the explosions.

"Perhaps that was the night my husband died," remarked Diana, winningly. "At least he died with his hose in his hand."

All the men raised an eyebrow, chuckled and looked at each other knowingly. What a gal.

Vic Gordon entered with Jacko. Predictably, but to Fan's great embarrassment, Diana threw her arms around Jacko and cried: "I'm Fan's mother, darling. You were absolutely terrific."

Jacko smiled at Fan and looked bashfully at his boots.

Could have been worse, thought Vic Gordon. This good-old pearly queen has diverted all the attention from the real girl friend.

Then he glanced at Jacko and Fan, holding both hands and looking shyly at each other, and groaned inwardly. Vic Gordon had been around. He knew the signs.

This lovely, lissom young lady could cost us five grand on the turnstiles every Tuesday, if thousands of Jacko's girl followers believe he's betrayed them and stay away in protest.

ATTENDANCES didn't dip. Even more fans flocked to speedway each weeknight in the metropolitan evening sunsets.

London was at last breaking out of its immediate post-war stupor. There was a budding sense of optimism, fired by the wedding of Princess Elizabeth the winter before, freshly stoked by news of her pregnancy. London was agog about the first post-war Olympic Games at Wembley.

Milk rationing had eased, clothing allowance had risen, the new National Heath Service started, birthrate was booming.

Things were beginning to look up.

Not that Fan and Jacko were aware of the mellowing mood. They were in a world of their own, a world oblivious to their romance.

They were secret, discreet lovers.

Every weekend they would steal away, usually to the New Forest which held a special attraction for them. They returned to their first lovenest in Rufus Stone. They discovered a lovely thatched pub called the Sir John Barleycorn in Cadnam, another hidden haunt in the village of Burley, where the ponies actually strolled into the bar and tried to steal food from your plate.

Fan wanted to visit and learn about Christchurch priory with its spectacular stained glass windows. Jacko wondered what poor old O'Reilly, with his religious rantings, would have made of it.

Fan and her mum were weekly directors' box guests each Tuesday. Diana attracted all the attention. She always had.

Jacko quietly arranged for Fan to sit on her own in the restaurant when the

Hammers visited New Cross. She travelled by Tube down the Old Kent Road to the tiny but tightly packed South London circuit.

New Cross were way out on top of the league, steamrollering all opposition on their tricky home track. West Ham were depleted by injuries and Fan watched wide-eyed as Jacko virtually singlehandedly battled the rampaging home riders.

Idiotically, she found herself shouting like a fourth-bend raver.

As Jacko slowed and tried to shield his team partner up front she heard herself saying "Jacko, Jacko, wait for Cliff, wait for him!" Then as two New Cross riders in their orange and black Maltese Cross body colours came charging up. "Jacko, don't wait for Cliff. Go, go!" She could hardly believe her own behaviour.

In his national match report, Barney Stacey wrote:

West Ham's brilliant young Jacko Rintzen, the kid they call The Outback Rocket, gave this one-sided match its lift off.

He saved Hammers from a rout and flustered the feathers of the New Cross vultures, expecting to pick the corpse of the understrength Hammers.

His bold, fearless tactics saved this match from being a disaster for another Full House down the Old Kent Road.

On this form, Rintzen must start favourite to win the Riders Championship, setting the record straight after being so cruelly robbed of his chance by his freak WWII debility last autumn.

After the New Cross meeting, Jacko quietly picked up Fan at the Elephant & Castle. They drove into Kent, found a hotel just off the A2 and talked for hours, as lovers do, lying in the darkness.

Fan whispered: "What will you do when you finish with speedway, Jacko?"

"Never really thought about it."

"But you must have some sort of plan, some ambition."

"Nah not at all. I'm doing everything I ever dreamed of. Fact, it's worked out better than I ever imagined. But what about you? You give the impression you really want to go places."

"Oh, I do, I do. I've got to get away from the East End of London. I've been lucky enough to have seen other places and heard about them."

Jacko knew Fan had a fascination for foreign places. She had taken him to the pictures at the Odeon, Gants Hill (now Jacko didn't have to queue for admission because he could afford to pay 3s 6d each for balcony seats) and seen her reverence for the USA.

"My Mum knew a lot of Americans during the war. She was very popular with them. They told me about California and New York and funny places like Nebraska, I'd love to see it all," she seemed slightly breathless.

"Ever fancy Aussie?"

"Gosh, yes, now that I've got you. It always seemed to be right out of reach, the other side of the planet. But now anything seems possible. I never thought life could be so exciting."

"Seems mighty good to me, too"

"Oh, please take me to your cattle station. I know I'll love it as long as you're there."

"Whoa up a while, it isn't my station. I'm just a hand. It belongs to Kerslake."

"Yes, but didn't you tell me he adopted you. And that he hasn't got a single relative. So he's bound to want you to take it over eventually. I could come and keep house for you." She giggled throatily.

The thought that he might be Kerslake's heir had never faintly occurred to Jacko.

"Jeez, what a thought. Do you really think the old bugger would do that?" he gasped.

"I think you're more to him than you realise," said Fan. "But you will always mean more to me."

"Yahoo, I'll make you the First Lady of Baranga,"howled Jacko. "And I'll bloody well show you the Yew-nited States of America, too."

It seemed impossible anything could come between them.

They fell into a regular weekend routine. Every Friday evening Jacko, hidden in a huge trilby and a wide-shouldered trench coat turned up at the collar, would pick up Fan when she returned home from the office.

They would drive out to their rural haunts, well away from the possibility of recognition and subsequent scandal.

On a Friday as London basked in Olympic fever, Jacko sneaked into Green Street to learn from Diana that Fan had been delayed for two hours by some major legal upheaval involving her firm in the Law Courts.

"She said for you to wait," said Diana. "You'd better come in."

Fan's mother was in an explosive mood. Dressed only in a silk dressing gown, she had been working on her make-up ready to go out to the West End to see Annie Get Your Gun with a silly old fool who had made a small fortune from war surplus. They were staying at the Mayfair Hotel afterwards.

But he had called with a late, very curt cancellation. Maybe his wife was in the know. Her weekend was torpedoed. Diana hated being on her own.

In frustration she had opened a bottle of French white wine from a consignment one of her wideboy chums had mysteriously acquired from some dark dockside deal.

She was halfway down the bottle when Jacko arrived.

Now when Diana started drinking, her hormones galloped around in hobnail boots.

She was seething with resentment. Here she was, stuck in bloody Green Street for the weekend, while her daughter was slinking off for a dirty weekend with this incredibly attractive guy, relaxed but still looking lithe and dangerous on her settee reading the speedway reports in the *Stratford Express* and *East London Advertiser.*

She couldn't help herself. She jumped on him, like an alley cat pouncing on a dozy dormouse.

Jacko could control the meanest mustang, the most skittish stallion, an Army Service motorbike on one wheel, and the most powerful pound-for-pound racing engine in the world at peak performance.

But he could not control a maneater like Diana Harris at her peak performance.

SEXUALLY Jacko was more mouse than rat, more mug than monster.

In almost total innocence, he had developed an ironclad conscience over casual acts of physical contact.

His naivety dated back to his first experience of feminine wiles when Bongo Drumma's schoolgirl sister had unexpectedly invaded his bedroom.

Jacko had been racked with guilt after that event, but the subject was never mentioned. Everyone had acted perfectly naturally ever since. Bel Drumma treated him like a longlost brother.

He thought this must be the right sort of way everyone handled it.

That bit of naughty nonsense with Diana would surely be the same. Surely. He was bewildered about how it had happened. How had the woman managed to get him out of his pants? He would sooner have tumbled his old school Marm than Fan's mother. God, she was an old woman. How had it happened?

Before he had met Fan, Jacko considered sex like defecating in the outback: you did it, felt better for it, buried it and forgot about it. It had nothing to do with love.

This attitude was inured by the Track Spare Code that grew up in the wild, sexually uninhibited post-war days in British speedway. He had been unable to avoid brushes with 'wild childs' like Yo Yo Knickers, Doormat Dora and Miss Gooey Gusset of Grays Thurrock. But any pangs of guilt Jacko experienced just drifted away, like tumbleweed.

It was totally different with Fan, of course. Jacko felt their relationship was way above a physical attraction. Fan was girl perfection. If your motor was working perfectly, you didn't need the spare.

Jacko, feeling uncomfortably dirty, allowed his thoughts to drift along these lines, crouched with his coat collars turned up in his wagon, parked in the jigsaw jungle of back streets behind Diana's Green Street shop.

Diana had said: "You'd better wait outside. I'll make sure I'm in the bath when Fan gets home."

Jacko felt like he needed a bath too but decided not to dwell guiltily over his surprise, totally stupid seduction. It was just like Bel Drumma. And would surely go away just like that.

He was hopelessly too unfamiliar with women to understand that very few of them thought like that…

Besides, he had other things on his mind.

Vic Gordon had invited Fan and Jacko for the weekend at his farm at Stock, a very English village with a duck pond and a thatched pub haunted by the ghost of an ostler, deep in the Essex countryside. They also planned to visit High Beech in the Epping Forest, scene of the first speedway meeting in Britain in February 1928.

Vic kept two prime roan hunters in his stable so Jacko had been invited to a brisk gallop and workout. He was excited at the prospect of handling a different form of horse power again. Fan had rightly marvelled at his way with horses. He wanted to teach her to horse ride. That was much more important than a bit of rough and tumble on a settee.

Then the following weekend he would not be able to see Fan. That was a real pain. Jacko loved their discreet, stolen moments together. But he had agreed his first meeting in Continental Europe.

West Ham had staged an Olympiad international event, to link loosely with events at Wembley. Speedway racing had been forced out of Empire Stadium for the 1948 Olympics, but would return in September in time for the Riders Championship Final. Jacko had that on his mind too.

In an effort to give the Olympiad meeting a more international flavour, the West Ham management had drafted in two Dutch riders. They were charming fellows, reasonable motor cyclists but hopelessly outclassed by the granite-hard professional standards in Britain.

Jacko learned that when the Nazis had invaded Holland, the Dutch riders had buried their JAP speedway engines under a tulip field, to avoid their being claimed by the occupation army for military use. They had remained hidden for five years.

Their motors sounded and performed like there were still tulip bulbs sprouting from the carburettors.

But the Dutch invited a British speedway party back to appear at Rotterdam and insisted that Jacko be included. They would claim he had Dutch ancestry.

"You look a bit like a Dutchman, Jacko," said one.

Post-war speedway promoters worldwide did not believe in allowing the truth to get in the way of crowd-pulling publicity.

Word was over 70,000 fans were fighting for tickets to see Jacko and other British League stars on Sunday – the Dutch did not have Britain's strict Sunday observance restrictions.

So Jacko desperately erased the ugly memory of Diana from his mind as Fan dashed back, grabbed an overnight bag, and they slipped away for another weekend together.

They were not to know it was their last.

WITH THE WEEKEND stretching depressingly ahead, Fan missed Jacko achingly. They had not missed a Sunday together since their original Hamble ramble. But he was away trailblazing in Holland.

Diana, too, was flopping around. She hated the dreary religious routine of 1940s Sundays.

She made a pot of tea – it was still difficult to obtain coffee. Then mother and daughter lapsed naturally into a good old girlie gossip and giggle.

Diana considered she had always been a pretty good mate for Fan. They had few secrets, behaved more like sisters. Men and sex were never hushed-up subjects. Diana had never seen Fan, who had often appeared introverted in her presence, more vital, full of the joys of living. She knew her daughter had never been lacking boyfriends. But now she seemed, well, somehow fulfilled.

It was fun sharing a frivolous conversation.

Diana had been taken to the ballet the night before at Sadlers Wells. The fine arts appealed to her acute sense of social climbing.

Back home she became the old Diana.

She giggled: "Oh, Fan. You should have seen the male dancers. Their bums! Quite the most attractive I've ever seen."

Fan smiled enigmatically: "I think my Jacko has got the cutest bum ever," she said dreamily.

113

"Yes, darling, particularly when you consider all those awful bullet wounds."

A silence. A nasty, loaded silence. Fan stared sharply at her mother. She wasn't dreamy any more.

"How do you know about his wounds? How did you know? How?"

Cursing her carelessness, Diana replied airily: "Oh, I read about them somewhere."

"No you didn't, you didn't. He makes sure they're never mentioned."

"Oh, he must have told me."

"No, he didn't, he didn't. He never talks about them. How did you know? How?"

"It must have cropped up somewhere. You must have told me. Maybe the doctor at West Ham? Anyway, it doesn't matter…" Diana's sentence died abruptly as she saw the awful anguish carved into her daughter's face.

"Mum, mum, please tell me it isn't what I'm thinking. Please. There's only one way you could know about his scars. You didn't, you couldn't, surely. It was that weekend when I was late, wasn't it? I thought it was funny he was waiting outside and you were in the bath. God, it's disgusting YOU and Jacko … Not Jacko, mum, please."

Terrible tears were spilling on to her housecoat.

"Oh, for God's sake, Ann" – Diana had only called her that half a dozen times in twenty years – "Don't be so hysterical. It was just one of those things. You know what men are like."

"I know what *you* are like!" Fan was out of control. "You're twisted, depraved. He was mine. You know how I feel about Jacko. I thought he was different. I love him. But you've ruined it forever. Forever."

"You're behaving like a bloody schoolgirl. I warned you about dirt track riders right from the start. He's only an Australian farm hand. He'll have dozens of randy little floozies at every stadium in the country. You'll be better off without him. I've done you a favour."

But Fan was whispering: "Not my Jacko. Not him. And my mother. No, no…"

She disappeared into her room and collapsed on the bed.

Diana heard her sobbing uncontrollably for over an hour and felt she had to get away. She knew the very sight of her was fanning the flames.

She had an old boy friend, a pub landlord in Leigh on Sea, whom she often used as an escape.

She knocked gently on Fan's door and said: "I'm driving down to see my friend in Leigh on Sea. I'll be back later."

"I don't care if you drive off a cliff." Diana bit her lip at the sheer hatred in her daughter's reply.

Across the North Sea, thousands of Dutch spectators were queuing five deep to see the famous Australian superhero who was quietly checking his tyre pressures in a corner of the pits.

He was completely unaware that the first – and last – real love in his life had been blown apart.

Destroyed by a ballet dancer's buttocks.

DIANA was not a good driver and the Standard Eight she had been given for services rendered was not in particularly serviceable condition. There were many lethal wagons on the road after the war.

Travelling down the lengthy ribbon of dual carriageway of the A127 Southend Arterial Road, she had time to realise the enormity of what she had caused. Damn my stupid drinking, damn him, he could have stopped me, damn everything.

Diana found her eyes welling up.

She ran off the road on the steep left hand climb just before Rayleigh. The car hit the kerb, then the ditch, started disintergrating and turned over. Diana was thrown clean through the windscreen.

The Belle of Boleyn had escaped from Green Street forever.

CHAPTER 13

BEFORE his first public appearance at White City, Ritchie's demolition boss called him to his office.

A self-made millionaire and rabid Scot, James McMechin, a member at Gleneagles and the Scottish FA committee, presented Ritchie with a neckerchief of Mackay tartan.

"That's your lucky charm, son," he said. "Always wear it when you're racing."

"I'll not be needing luck, sir," replied Ritchie. "As long as I get a chance I'll make my own luck."

After his first junior rides, he was swiftly aware that the Glasgwegian crowds were willing him to succeed. They were desperate for a local hero. They wanted a winner, a cinder track equivalent of the Wembley Wizards.

They noted and appreciated his touch of tartan. Ritchie rode with it blowing in his slipstream. Somebody called him the Tartan Tearaway.

He was mobbed by gangs of girl fans prowling the pits carpark and did nothing to fight off their attacks. But it was still good old whambam snatched sex. And they were no ladies. Just scrubbers. It was all riproaring fun but Ritchie still nurtured grander notions.

He won a place in the Tigers team within weeks. Glasgow always had problems staffing their line-up. Local boys, like Ritchie, were appearing only recently. For all the previous years, the locals simply could not afford the outlay for speedway equipment. The Glasgow management had been forced to attract Englishmen, who were not keen to live in Scotland or make a lengthy round trip for 'home' meetings; or wandering Australians, who were targeted by more attractive offers at more fashionable clubs.

So a born and bred Glasgwegian Tiger was a godsent.

The Glasgow Evening Chronicle called him Speedway's First Potential Great Scot.

"You've a real chance to make something of yourself," his boss McMechin said. "I'll nae bother if you take time off. Go and be a winner."

Within a month of going on the Tigers payroll, Ritchie was a winner, having stashed away enough money to fulfil one of his ambitions. He booked a table for dinner at the LMS Hotel and, wearing his father's Sunday suit and tie, presented himself to the head waiter. His former sniffy boss had long gone so Ritchie was shown to a table without the blink of an eye.

A waitress recognised him from Glasgow speedway and asked him to sign a menu.

Making progress in life, thought Ritchie, spooning soup. But I'm dining alone. Next time I come here I'm going to be escorting a stylish wee bit of stuff.

SUMMER faded with smog still curtaining the Clyde, but the speedway season was ending too swiftly for Ritchie.

Established in the Tigers team, earning four times as much money as he had drawn as a truck driver, slapping and tickling the girls to a frazzle every week, his flowing tartan scarf became the iconic feature of Scottish speedway.

The Evening Chronicle ran a poll for The Most Popular Tiger, which Ritchie won by a distance.

Armed with a copy of the newspaper, he sought an interview with boss Iain Harman in his office. Harman was the most brilliant of the post-war, new generation promoters, with a flair for showmanship and a reputation for astute management. The boss's secretary, Mrs Bess Coleman, well-heeled, in her thirties, split from an executive husband in the whisky distribution business, had lengthy experience of cheeky, confident chat from upstart speedmen.

"Come to talk new terms?" she inquired, with a dazzling smile.

"Aye, maybe."

"A word of warning, sunshine. The boss is in a filthy mood this morning. He's been tied with Enviromental Officers talking about noise levels on race nights – and angry husbands who reckon their wives are deserting them for speedway! Nothing to do with your off track shennangans of course. . ." Ritchie did not care much for that threat, but made the first move once admitted to see the boss.

"See this vote," he said. "I'm more popular wie the folk than the team captain or yon Australian topscorer. That should be worth something extra."

"That would be illegal," replied Harman, sourly. "You get paid the rate according to the contract you signed. You're doing all right."

"That's bollocks. There are blokes at other tracks getting well above the rate. I know there are blokes at Glasgow getting extra too."

Harman snorted. "There are blokes in the Glasgow team getting more points than you."

"Aye, maybe. But I'm more popular. See what the fans think in the paper. You're getting me on the cheap. I only live around the corner but you're shelling out return air fares for the two Australians in the team.

"I reckon I could do better at another track. They're all getting over the odds at Edinburgh. And there's a lot of talk about another track in Glasgow next year. They'd jump at the chance to sign a local boy."

The Glasgow boss smiled like a shark. "Don't try to be a smart-ass, Ritchie," he replied. "I'm the one opening that new track at Ashfield although the public will never know. There'll be a puppet in charge. And you're not going there. I'm not having you taking five thousand Tigers fans across the city. So what do you think you're worth extra?"

Ritchie did not hesitate.

"A return fare to Australia," he said. "That way I'm not breaking any contract."

After much discussion with the Australians in the Glasgow team, Ritchie was sure he could earn a reasonable crust as a freelance racing on tracks Down Under during the British close season.

A wanderlust bug had been chewing him. He felt sure he was going places in speedway. He certainly did not want to spend another perishingly dire winter driving dumper trucks around Glasgow. It had been no great surprise to him when the secretary lady had mentioned the threat of angry husbands.

Ritchie felt the time might be appropriate to get out of town.

Twelve thousand miles away should be a safe distance.

"Well, did you get what you wanted, big boy?" asked Mrs Coleman winningly as he passed her desk.

"Aye, and now if only I could have you, Mrs Coleman, my life would be complete," he replied.

The secretary looked at her fingernails, shook her head slowly and said: "Your bum's out the window."

WIRELESS OFFICER Patrick Dean had never before received a MarconiGram addressed to his cross-channel ferry while at sea. Nothing much seemed to happen on his twice-daily run between Tilbury and Ostend. He whiled away the boredom tuned into this new-fangled American Forces Network, playing crazy new music be-bop.

But it was definitely a morse message for his ship marked Most Urgent and addressed to a passenger called J. Rintzel.

The ship's speaker requested Jacko to report immediately to the Radio Office on Deck A.

Jacko and the rest of the British speedway party were relaxing in one of the ferry's saloons. They were in good humour.

Their visit to Rotterdam had been a storming success. Dutch promoters were not so security conscious as hysteria-hardened British track bosses. Jacko had been mobbed and trapped by rampaging Dutch fans, needing to be rescued after nearly half an hour. Ben Silva had played his plonker and sung All My Life I've Wanted To Be A Barrowboy over the track tannoy, to a rapturous reception.

Uproarious veteran Phil Bishop – the same character who had swum ashore in Aden before the war and nearly been eaten by sharks – had been up to his hospital pranks in Holland. An old fashioned leg trail stylist, quite the most spectacular Jacko had ever seen, he was prone to get involved in horrendous pile-ups and end in hospital.

He'd broken his foot and ankle bones in Rotterdam but absconded from hospital in the dead of night, having bought the clothes of the bewildered Dutchman in the next bed.

But he had insisted he was only paying for one shoe. He couldn't get the other over the plastercast. The hospitalised Dutchman was left believing all Englishmen were completely mad.

Jacko loved all these adventures, all these characters. But when he heard his name over the speaker, he shrugged and went to see what could possibly be so important to call him while bucketing about in the North Sea.

The message was from Gordon, West Ham Speedway. It read:

REPORT IMMEDIATELY TO WEST HAM SPEEDWAY OFFICE ON YOUR RETURN STOP. DO NOT, REPEAT NOT, CONTACT OR SPEAK TO ANYONE STOP. URGENTEST.

The only reason Jacko figured to create such drama was maybe Wembley Lions had made a record transfer bid for his services. They were not having a very successful season.

Vic Gordon was sitting at his desk looking mighty grim. Mighty grim. Silently he passed a copy of that morning's Stratford Express across the desk.

The front page splash screamed Horror Death Of Green Street Glamour Girl. Jacko felt his blood icing up and draining as he read:

Well-known, popular Green Street florist Diana Harris was tragically killed when her car somersaulted off the A127 Southend Arterial Road yesterday afternoon.

Mrs Harris was the widow of the former Chief Fireman at East Ham, Reg Harris and highly regarded as an East End beauty and socialite.

Unconfirmed reports indicate she was decapitated in the accident. The cause of the tragedy has not yet been established.

Her only daughter Ann was yesterday being comforted by relatives at Upminster.

There was a five-column photograph, which looked like a Hollywood handout, spread across the page.

The story continued with tributes to Diana from fellow Green Street traders and established local figures who had known her. But Jacko did not want to read any more.

He could think only of Fan.

Vic Gordon soon shattered those thoughts. Vic had been tipped off about the story by a sub-editor contact at the newspaper, warning him there were stories circulating that Diana had recently been identified regularly in the directors' box at West Ham Speedway.

Vic, who did not live too far from Upminster, had visited Fan.

And immediately realised a very swift cover-up was essential.

He said to Jacko: "I've seen Fan and you better not go within a million miles of her.

"She's spitting bile, blaming you for everything. She's talking riddles, saying it would have been best if some snake had got you. She says she never, ever wants to see you again. Ranted on about you and her mum. I don't know what happened, but I don't want you to get mixed up in all this."

Secretly Vic was confident West Ham Speedway could avoid any scandal. Again the attention had been diverted from Fan. He did not tell Jacko that Fan had spitefully added: "Don't worry, Mr Gordon. I won't be involving your precious speedway. There's no way I want the world to know what a fool I've been."

Jacko thought bitterly the Track Spare Omerta Code had its limits.

But he felt he was honour bound to attend Diana's funeral, to try to reason with Fan. There might still be a glimmer... His indiscretion with her mother did not mean anything. He just couldn't handle her. Maybe Fan would listen to reason. In time.

The funeral was well attended at the huge East London cemetery, which ran for over a mile parallel with the Eastern Region mainline into Liverpool Street. Diana had been a very popular figure; there were bunches of successful looking men in expensive-looking overcoats eyeing each other suspiciously.

Hidden behind his high collar and oversized hat, Jacko stood at the very edge of the burial group. He was shocked, shattered, when he saw Fan. She looked like a tragic ghost. She seemed to have aged twenty years.

Seeing Jacko, Fan stormed across to him, her eyes blazing with hatred. As her mother's next of kin, she had had to identify Diana's body. The undertaker had cleaned her mother but could not remove traces of blood in her silver-blond hair. Fan knew it was an image that would stay with her for the rest of her days.

"What are you doing here? You bastard, you absolute bastard," she screamed. "You killed her, don't you know that? You killed her. You've taken my mum from me. She'd still be here but for you. You've wrecked my life. I'll never see you again, never think about you again You never happened. Never. Never."

Jacko did not know much about women but he knew Fan meant it.

There was only one place he could find sanctuary.

The gateman at West Ham Stadium asked him to sign a programme for his sister-in-law and admitted him into the huge empty, eerily silent stadium.

Jacko climbed to the top step on the terraces of the fourth corner, where he knew Fan had watched her first speedway.

He sat, placed both hands on his head, and dropped it between his knees.

Until that precise moment, only dogs and horses had made Jacko cry.

CHAPTER 14

RINT-ZENSATIONAL, wrote Rick Eldon in the Speedway Echo.

His page three leader blared:

Whatever Jacko Rintzen has been eating in recent weeks, I want in large dollops.

Since his return from Holland, he's gone from brilliant to downright unbeatable.

He seems to have found an incredible new motivation and inspiration from somewhere and his thrilling, sometimes reckless impetuosity has given a breath-taking new excitement to Tuesday race nights in London's dockland. And wherever he appears.

He seems to find grip, drive and power out of nowhere. Some of his flying starts have looked impossible.

All opponents see of The Outback Rocket these days is his back wheel.

He's an exhilarating spectacle and in this form a racing certainty to win the upcoming British Riders Championship Final, following his shockingly unlucky forced withdrawal 12 months ago.

Jacko, broken by the tragic events in his hushed-up private life, had escaped from his emotions in the only way he knew.

He shut off his memory and hurled himself totally into speedway racing.

Now there was something else to forget besides Bowz and Blue.

Vic Gordon insisted Jacko moved in with him. "I need to keep my eye on you," he said. Jacko was relieved to get away from Hamble. It had too many painful images. Nipper was about to move on, anyway.

Realistically, Gordon knew West Ham and Jacko had been fortunate to escape involvement in the Diana Harris tragedy. He had made quiet inquiries and learned Ann was planning to move to Paris with a job as secretary at the new NATO HQ. He did not tell Jacko.

The whole affair was drifting away and dying like an exhaust echo.

Typically, Gordon, who always considered every angle, began thinking maybe it would have been more sensational publicity if he had promoted Jacko as a sort of randy ragdoll in a tug o'war between mother-and-daughter sex rivals.

He admitted to himself he did not need to manufacture publicity for Master Rintzen. Now the Olympics had ended and Don Bradman had retired, Jacko and his exploits were backpage headline hoggers daily. He even attracted offers from the British film industry.

Still the urchin kid brother of Hollywood, the post-war British film business attempted to cash in and capture the flavour of the sporting fervour of the era with a series of monochrome mini epics about the worlds of backstreet boxing, Test cricket, and speedway racing.

Filmed mainly at New Cross, the speedway offering was a 100-minute saga called 'Once A Jolly Swagman', but also known as 'Maniacs on Wheels' after a plotline with one of the stars highsiding and suffering brain damage.

Film makers Wessex Film Corporation had built a very special track at Elstree Studios: it only had a start and one corner. It was the oddest, smallest track ever.

Although one or two of the actors in the movie, like Bill Owen, actually had competitive motor racing experience, all of the racing scenes used 'doubles'for the stars. Several of the West Ham juniors were on permanent standby for weeks. At £10 a day they were certainly not complaining nor hurrying the situation. Vic Gordon would not allow his regular team men to be thus distracted.

Towards the end of shooting the director, an artistic, expansive chap called Jack Lee, needed one special scene of a rider wheelie-ing spectacularly the length of one straight. He did not think any of his doubles were skilful enough.

Diplomatically, he asked them: "Who is the best rider on one wheel in London?"

Unanimously, the West Ham juniors said: "Gotta be Rintzen. Nobody has control like him. He's a wheelie whiz. Word is he actually did a wheelie through Rommel's headquarters during the war."

Vic Gordon granted special permission for Jacko to spend a day filming at Elstree, provided The Rank Organisation paid him £100 and insured him for £50,000. Then he issued a Press Bulletin saying: Jacko, worth £1000 for every yard he travels on one wheel. It made a page lead in the London evening newspapers.

It was quite an event when Jacko did his party piece for the cameras. Actors, extras and technicians from adjoining sets drifted over to watch; there were characters in evening dress, Gaiety Girls, extras in costumes from the Napoleonic wars.

Jacko performed sufficiently well in one take. But the director insisted on another hour of takes. "We're not paying out a hundred quid for less than ten seconds," he mumbled.

"This bloke is a bit special on a bike, isn't he?" observed a cameraman.

"He should be in show business."

"He already is," said one of the rider doubles. "You should come to West Ham on a Tuesday and see."

It was an interesting diversion for Jacko. Another publicity coup for the Hammers. But he had other, more important matters on his mind.

Now the Big Night at Wembley was coming up. If Jacko wins that, thought Vic Gordon, we could get over 80,000 frenzied fans paying at the turnstiles at West Ham to welcome him home…

ALTHOUGH no longer involved in a feverish day-to-day racing existence, Bryan Nipper Corbin was an incorrigible wheeler-dealer, always sniffing about to earn a quid, make new contacts.

He had moved house from Hamble down to Sandbanks, an appropriately named sand-dune peninsula bordering the huge, natural but shallow Poole Harbour on the Dorset coast.

"It's a bit desolate, moosh", he said to Jacko when inviting him down. "Everyone reckons the sea will wash it away with a decent high tide. But I reckon property prices will go up there and I can make money."

Nipper had also established an involvement with the new speedway club, the Poole Pirates, who had opened in the Third Division, British speedway's lowest tier, in the spring. The 420-yard track had formerly been a banked cycle circuit and had been lovingly converted for high powered, high octane activity.

"It's a dream," said Nipper. "Come and stay for the weekend, and on Monday night the Poole management will pay you readies to establish a one-lap record and present a few prizes. Good way to prepare for Wembley. No problems, no pressure, moosh."

It was a superb set-up. Jacko was given a delirious reception by over 7,000 fans, wedged shoulder-to-shoulder in the town-centre stadium, with steam trains chuffing picturesquely behind the tumbledown main stand. Jacko was the biggest speedway name yet to appear at the Dorset track. He was regarded with god-like reverence.

The Pirates side were lovely, friendly local boys, led by a smiling, fair-haired former RAF rear gunner whom Jacko thought could comfortably have commanded a team place in Division I.

The track racing surface was as good as Jacko had known. A featherbed. Jacko had wings as he duly set a one-lap record.

Wouldn't mind the British Final being staged here, he thought.

He had to travel back that night, ride his regular home fixture at West Ham, then concentrate on the British Championship Final at Wembley on Thursday.

Jacko drove back through the New Forest, still exorcising the ghosts of recent experiences in those parts, concentrating his thoughts on Chinners getting his clutch absolutely perfect for Wembley.

Historically, the New Forest ponies with which Jacko had formed an immediate bonding, had freedom to wander the forest. They had been there before roads had been constructed. But they wandered onto the roads, often seeking food from motorists. Accidents had become a growing problem as traffic increased. Hundreds of ponies had perished.

Long-drawn-out discussions between the road safety authorities and the Forest verderers about fencing off the roads had repeatedly stalled in the face of indignation from animal lovers.

So the ponies continued to roam, innocently, on the main roads, causing unpleasant accidents.

Jacko, equine expert though he was, was not to know that New Forest ponies tended to gather in the forest valleys, the dips, in little packs, and when their leader went, galloped across in numbers.

He had just reached the bottom of the long, gradual dip between Picket Post and Cadnam when the leader of the pack decided to go.

Jacko's reflexes miraculously enabled his hard-braking wagon to swerve and avoid the main pack. But nothing he could do avoided clipping the rear leg of the very last pony in the pack, which was sent spinning.

Jacko bumped to a stop on the grass verge, cracking his right shoulder on the driver's door.

Another nightmare. There seemed no end of them. Jacko was distraught when he viewed the damage he'd done. The poor pony's leg was pulped. Although his shoulder

126

was throbbing with pain, he sat for over an hour, trying to calm the distressed animal, which wasn't very old, waiting for a vet to arrive to end the agony.

It was Bowz all over again.

With misty eyes, Jacko wondered bitterly how many more tragedies were waiting to knock his block off and break his heart.

FOR THE SECOND successive year, Vic Gordon had to withdraw Jacko from the big Wembley occasion. This, he thought, is getting to be a bloody farce. He'd never known a bloke to get such devastating luck.

Jacko's collarbone was broken. Vic believed Jacko might have tried to have ridden, heavily strapped. But the real injury was mental.

Jacko was wrecked. He had caused the awful death of a living creature. He shut himself in his room, wouldn't talk, wouldn't eat. Penitently, he took a blanket and slept in the straw with Vic's horses in the stable. In the wake of his recent emotional explosions, Vic Gordon was concerned he might top himself.

He forgot about a bumper crowd to greet Jacko at West Ham. He had to get him on a plane home, away from the horrors that haunted him in Britain, and hope the more uncomplicated life of the outback would ease his torment.

Before the start of next season…

Barney Stacey lamented in the Speedway Gazette:

Once again the gods have ganged up and cudgelled the dreams of an unassuming kid from the back of nowhere.

Wembley lost its billtopping star for the second successive year as Jacko Rintzen was robbed of his chance of glory by another crazy, fickle flip of Fate.

But he will surely, surely come again. Last year, disaster. This year, double disaster.

But to steal a phrase from a much more sinister figure of the 20th Century, maybe tomorrow, the world!

Speedway's authorities had decided that in 1949 there would be sufficient international competition to revive the Championship of the World.

Maybe Jacko was destined for the very big one, the ultimate. To assume the global crown, which technically still belonged to his prewar inspiration, fellow Australian Bluey Wilkinson, killed in a road accident early in the war.

Only Vic Gordon saw Jacko on to the plane home.

"It can only get better, Jacko," he said. "We all get years best forgotten. Remember you've earned nearly five grand racing. You're a wealthy boy. What will you do with the money? Buy some land? Stud farm? Sydney Harbour Bridge?"

"I'm having thoughts about that," said Jacko, quietly.

OLD MOKEY the mule had to admit that life wasn't so bad after all.

After a lifetime working literally until he dropped in a Welsh coal yard, he had landed in clover. Initially, he had been led into a muddy, windy field and left with a couple of equally pitiful former pit ponies, which were braying gratefully simply to be out in the daylight.

When a wagon had arrived, and a group of Two Legs pointed at them meaningfully, he had thought it was all to do with something called a Knackermaster. Mokey wasn't sure what it meant. None of his pals who were taken to find out had ever returned to report.

But Mokey and his indomitable pit pony partners had been driven to a place called Godalming, and a new home called Mule Terrain. Mokey thought this must be mule heaven.

There was a warm stable, with straw, and feed, and fresh water. There were wonderful Two Leg females in beige riding breeches who had blankets, and brushes and cloths to wipe them and sometimes even carrots. And apples. And sometimes something called chocolate. Mokey had never known chocolate before – sweets were still rationed. He thought he could get used to it. There was a Two Legs in a white coat who looked at their teeth. He was kind and caring, made a mule feel like a thoroughbred.

And a lazy sloping field, with a towering oak tree clump for shade, where Mokey was standing happily with a crazy old donkey that had been used for rides on the beach before the war. Another cousin had arrived from the New Forest. He'd been hurt in a road accident, but looked after by the White Coat Two Legs. He'd been a bit wild, but had settled into their cosy existence.

They all gazed contentedly at unusual activity up by the stable, where the Two Legs in breeches were making an enormous fuss of a visitor.

Mokey noticed he had a thatch of hair that looked rather like the straw in his warm, comfortable stall.

Maybe this is the Two Legs he had heard the Beige Breeches talk so much about. The Two Legs who was responsible for and paid to keep Mule Terrain going. They called him Benny Factor or something. Now they seemed to be calling him Jacko

Certainly like the look of him, thought Mokey. There's something about him…

I think I'll just amble up to the stables and give him a nuzzle.

CHAPTER 15

INEVITABLY, Stan Prince was called back by Wembley to start the 1948 season as reserve in the Lions senior side.

He had become a dad, a squawking son christened Philip Stanley because Dorry and her mum thought he should be named after that handsome Greek who had married Princess Elizabeth.

Stan still did the odd copy-taking shift, but increasingly spent more time in the JAP workshops. He did not trust his machinery with anyone else. Dorry thought it an unacceptable extravagance paying for a mechanic, too.

He concentrated on adapting his machinery to suit his style. Slightly lower gearing for starting, a tighter inside line. He worked for days getting his footrest right. He perfected his clutch, experimented with handlebars. He always stripped and cleaned his motor after meetings before bedding down, no matter how late the hour.

It was rewarding when mechanics at JAP and senior members of the Wembley side asked his advice. He was becoming a pro.

Because the 1948 Olympics took over Wembley until September, the Lions had to stage their home meetings at Wimbledon. That suited Stan. Wimbledon was only a yard longer than Eastbourne. He felt immediately at home, relished the similarity and soon won promotion into the team.

The Speedway Gazette reported:

Brightest angle of a disappointing season for the once mighty but now temporarily homeless Lions has been the improvement of their local boy discovery Stan Prince.

It isn't widely known that in his soccer playing days he was known as 'The Dribbler', modelling himself on the great Stanley Matthews.

He's brought that nickname into speedway. He dribbles around on the white line, cornering on rails. It's unspectacular but mighty effective. He's picking up a lot of wins.

Unquestionably, Stan was more a force on Britain's smaller circuits: Wimbledon, Harringay, New Cross. On the bigger brethren, Bradford, Belle Vue and West Ham, he was not so hot. His only sight of Jacko Rintzen at West Ham was a flapping white scarf and his back wheel disappearing in the distance. But that applied to most blokes.

By September when the Lions moved back to Empire Stadium, Stan was able to slap a four-hundred pound deposit on a semi-detached, 1920s-style house off the Bridgewater Road, near Sudbury Golf Course. He adapted the integral garage into a fully-equipped heated workshop. He did not need the airing cupboard to store his motors in the close season.

He was a Wembley local. He could walk to the stadium past the hospital and Wembley Central station.

Stan wallowed in the traditions and Wembley legends. He loved the tale of the genuine Wembley Lion. It occurred pre-war when Wembley's fierce North London rivals, the Harringay Tigers, produced a life-sized stuffed tiger as a team mascot.

Wembley had to go one better. Their great supremo Arthur Elvin deputed his staff to go and find a real live lion for their mascot.

They found a cub at a place called Chapman's Circus, which they were assured was "tame and affectionate, just like a well-trained dog."

When he was delivered to boss Elvin, purring like a big pussycat, the Wembley chief looked pensive when he learned he was nine months old.

"They start killing at twelve months," he warned. "He might not be our mascot for long." But the Wembley publicity office banged off dozens of pictures with team riders and settled the cub down in a specially reinforced segment of the greyhound kennels at the stadium.

The next morning staff discovered the cub had completely wrecked his makeshift home. When they contacted his circus home, the trainer diffidently observed: "Yes, he's probably missing his twin sister. He'll be okay when he's back with her." But on the way back to the circus, he attacked one of the Wembley staff, mangling and mauling his leg.

"Hmm, maybe best not to work with live animals," said Arthur Elvin. "West Ham had a similar problem with racing cheetahs. One tried to eat a greyhound."

There was another apparently apocryphal Wembley legend that Stan, living locally, was able to check out. Stories persisted that before Empire Stadium had been constructed for the British Exhibition in the early 1920s there had been a large pond on the site, frequented by herons and other birdlife.

The pond had been cemented over to form part of the car park. But while the concrete was still wet a flight of birds reappeared and had tried to land. Workmen had left their skidded landing grooves in the cement, a testimony to life at Wembley pre-Stadium.

Stan walked right around the stadium and actually found claw marks in the top surface of the car park, in a corner between the pits and Turnstiles A and B.

There always seemed something special about Wembley. Stan watched with fascination as the Lions management introduced a rocket bike to a gawping crowd. Boss Johnson had even found a genuine Professor of Ballistics to mastermind the experiment.

Enormous publicity accompanied the unveiling of the rocket bike at Empire Stadium, where it was to be ridden for the first time by the Lions captain.

Stan thought it looked like a conventional machine with twin exhausts stuffed with leftover rockets from Guy Fawkes Night. But with considerable drama, it rocketed from a standing start, then fizzled to a stop. Stan's mechanical logic insisted that rockets were designed to go in straight lines. And speedway bikes were basically created to be chain-driven. With rocket power, it was propulsion.

You could never have speedway without a tyre gripping. Or the noise of a sharp 500c.c. motor. Or the aroma of burning methanol.

Stan realised all the rocket bike ballyhoo was simply one good story to get the punters talking. It was all part of the Wembley tradition.

He really felt part of that Wembley tradition. He felt he belonged there. The feeling was reciprocated.

Speedway crowds always had a special place in their hearts for 'one of their own.' Stan was the new pride of the Lions.

One to watch for in 1949, said the pundits.

WESTERN AUSTRALIA was an absolute blast for Ritchie. He was welcomed rent-free into a sprawling, plantation bungalow of an expatriate Scottish family from Dundee, used their Holden pick-up, splashed for hours in their swimming pool, seduced both his hosts' ginger-haired daughters.

The Claremont track in Perth was bigger and wider at 640 yards than any Ritchie had previously experienced. A track where you needed to go fast. Ritchie learned to go very fast.

Handicap racing was all the rage, Ritchie quickly became a back marker. That's where the top money was to be earned. Starting sometimes 150 yards behind, you had to go past rivals double-quick.

His reputation flowed like his tartan scarf.

When the official English Lions touring team encountered injury problems, they asked Ritchie to step up as an emergency replacement. Although an attractive financial inducement was offered, Ritchie cabled back:

NO THANKS.

The captain of the tourists, a legendary figure from Belle Vue, called Ritchie long-distance.

"Are you crazy," he shouted. "You'll get three extra meetings at international money. You'll never get an offer like this back home. Not stuck away up in Glasgow."

"I'm no riding for England," said Ritchie.

"Why not?"

"Have you no heard of the Berwick massacre and the Highland Clearances? My old dad would skelp my backside if I ever pulled on an England colour.

"Thanks, but no way."

The story only made a couple of paragraphs in the Australian press. There were other freelancers the Lions could call up, although Ritchie's form had been better than any of them. But when the story hummed down the wires to Scotland, it was a banner splash.

Ritchie Tells Sassenachs To Get Stuffed!

From John O'Groats to Gretna Green, Ritchie became the toast of the Tartan nation. There were a couple of thousand fans and every Scottish newspaper waiting to greet him when he stepped off the train at Glasgow Central on his return.

Straight back to White City, he marched into bossman Harman's office and said: "I'm more popular than ever now. You are going to have to pay me over the odds."

In great good humour on his way out, he sprawled on the secretary's desk and said: "Ready for that date yet, Mrs Coleman? Now that I'm the nation's hero and sweetheart."

"Your bum's still out the window," she scoffed. "And the rain is battering on it."

But she could not help feeling amused by this saucy, sun-tanned scoundrel.

Those throwaway remarks about being the nation's hero proved to be surprisingly prophetic.

Ritchie's spell Down Under gave him a racer's edge on most of the other riders who had spent a lazy winter wrapped up listening to a Book At Bedtime on the radio.

He was a better balanced, fighting fit, more polished all-round performer and with ex-boss McMechin willingly stumping up for new equipment and old Joe Lowther manipulating the mechanical angles, Ritchie quickly became White City's top scorer and biggest box office attraction.

Mackay Is The Real McCoy, blazoned the headlines.

He was sure he was the biggest earner in the White City team but was conscious of all the nudging and whispering when he joined his dad for a dram.

"You'll need to go South to make real money, Ritchie," said the canny old boys at the bar. "Every successful Scottish sportsman has had to make his fortune in England."

Ritchie had been reared with an innate dislike of all things English. As a schoolboy in a gaunt Victorian building he had been given the impression England wanted to grind the Scots under, everyone was rich south of the border, and the weather hot.

Travelling to away matches at places like Newcastle, Sheffield and Fleetwood, Ritchie discovered it was not at all as he imagined. There was poverty and filthy weather like the grimmest quarter of the Gorbals.

He also discovered that English girls were just as randy and willing as the Glasgow Track Spares. And he knew most.

He dare not risk his trademark tartan scarf among the fans. It would have been ripped, snipped or nicked. But he relished the attention. And responded. And burning with ambition and ironclad confidence, he was itching to have a crack at the genuine bigtime.

Ritchie's growing track reputation was still a rumour to the big-money tracks in London. But whispered word circulated speedway that he was restless, looking for a move.

Bossman Harman summoned him to his office and eyed him wearily. "I knew right from the start you'd be a handful," he said. "Never satisfied. Glasgow belongs to you. But it isn't enough. You could be devoured by the sharks of speedway…"

"Aye, but at least I'll be swimming in the same water," replied Ritchie. "You cannae blame me for wanting to get on."

"The Scots will never forgive you for leaving," warned Harman.

"They will if I win the world title and they play Scotland The Brave at Wembley," said Ritchie. "I went to Hampden Park to see Scotland play England and they greeted all the guys who played for English teams like long lost sons.

"They'll forgive me if I'm a winner."

There's going to be no holding him, thought Harman.

Two weeks later, after Ritchie had been unbeaten through four meetings, Coventry, newly promoted into Division II and struggling to be competitive, made an over-the-top transfer bid for his services.

"It's a great track and set-up but hardly as big as Glasgow," said Ritchie. "I want bigger and better than that."

The same week he was invited to join the judging panel for the Belle of Rothesay beauty competition. One of his fellow panellists was Morag McGillivray, a slender beauty with waist-length auburn hair, one of Scotland's most respected folk singers. The Angel of Annan, she'd been called.

After the contest, irrepressible Ritchie grinned like a schoolboy and said: "I don't suppose I can offer an earthly dinner at our hotel. I've always wanted to walk into a posh restaurant with an angel on my arm."

Morag returned an equally schoolgirlish grin and replied: "I'm not hungry but I've always wanted to have a malt whisky with a Tiger."

THE SCOTTISH folk and traditional music community were not amused to learn their Angel of Annan was hobnobbing with a hooly like Ritchie Mackay.

Husky Highlanders with tree-trunk legs muttered darkly into bushy beards about the deflowering of Scotland's silver-voiced songbird by this tenement tearaway.

But when Morag appeared at a folk festival wearing one of Ritchie's Mackay tartan scarves slung loosely around her neck and then sang unaccompanied to a mesmerised 20,000 fans during the interval break at White City, it became very clear they were a couple. And she was in his thrall.

Ritchie had found his 'classy bit of stuff'. But although awed by her porcelain presence he was ill at ease. He was accustomed to rough trade. Morag was too much the lady, too inhibited for his liking.

But she had an unexpected art of exciting him. After one intense folk singing session near Kelvin Hall, she whispered: "Come on, Tiger. We're going stomping."

"Stomping? I fancied a malt."

But Morag steered him away from the nearest bar to a cellar in Bridalbon Street, Glasgow, called The Jive Dive, where they had a group of musicians called The Clydeside Cakewalkers playing a radically new sensation called traditional jazz. Well, it was new in Scotland although jazz originated nearly 100 years earlier when former negro slaves had picked up discarded musical instruments and played them in their own way after the American Civil War. Ritchie had heard American music on the American Forces Network Radio in BAOR. But he was not aware the US Forces exclusively broadcast what they considered to be 'white' music and jazz. Trad was still thought to be negro music, and rarely aired. The BBC considered a Vera Lynn record daringly revolutionary.

Prejudice certainly did not prevent white European disciples of the legends of New Orleans recreating the sounds of Basin Street. Even below the sloping cobbles of Bridalbon Street.

Most of the Scottish music Ritchie had experienced had an accordion involved somewhere. Even Morag's folk clubs.

But the atmosphere in The Jive Dive was wild, a different world. Ritchie could not help his foot tapping. Hey, this was all right.

One of the jazzmen, who had been playing skipping cadences on a clarinet, called out: "Hey, Morag. Morag McGillivray. Folks, we've got Scotland's greatest folk singer in tonight. Come on, Morag. Come and join us for a blast."

Morag shyly stepped on to the stage, avoiding pint tankards and empty beer bottles. Ritchie felt his jaw gaping. He had never heard her sing like this. The nightingale had become a wild songbird.

"I've gone away, baby.

"Gone away baby blues."

Her voice went through you like a tracer bullet. The reception was rapturous.

The Cakewalkers broke from blues time into a brisk, foot-tapping four-four rhythm and Morag belted out, aye, thought Ritchie, bloody belted out:

"Give me a pig's foot

"And a bottle of beer

"It's a hot time, in old town.

"Tonight."

Ritchie fancied her more strongly than ever before.

Before Morag left the stage despite cries for more, she whispered something in the ear of the clarinet player

"And now, folks, a special Dixieland tribute to another great Scottish guest, Mr

Ritchie Mackay, the star of Glasgow Tigers."

The band went blazing through 'Tiger Rag', the crowd clapped in time and Ritchie was surrounded by girls with long hair and chunky woollen sweaters, demanding autographs.

When he eventually got Morag alone, he said: "You were terrific. I've never heard you sing like that. Why d'you bother about all those speed bonny boats when you could be making a fortune singing like that all over the world? Why don't you always sing like that?"

"Because it's like whoring," replied Morag, gently.

"It's fun, but it would get you in the end. Anyway, I don't want to sing all over the world."

Ritchie's head was still echoing to the "hold that tiger, hold that tiger" raucous climax in the jazz club. There's going to be no holding this Tiger, he thought.

But Scotland had a hold on Morag. She was reluctant to leave the heather and glens. Ritchie talked wildly about moving to London, the bright lights, mighty money, the high life. He would be a star of the speedways, she would storm the stage. They would be unstoppable.

She simply shook her head when he invited her to go with him for a booking at West Ham. "I've got a festival at Ullapool booked," she said.

"But it's London, the bigtime," said Ritchie. "Surely you fancy sharing the experience?"

Morag realised it was the last thing she fancied and, suddenly, she needed her ain folk.

Ritchie headed South alone with only a tinge of regret. Och, she would still be there when he returned. If not, well, she had been a fun experience but hardly stirred his loins. And musically he preferred Buttons & Bows to all those fiddles and Wild Irish Rovers. Quite liked that trad stuff, too.

On his first sight of West Ham Stadium, towering among the cranes of Docklands, Ritchie knew this sort of set-up was where he needed to make an impact. It was the place to be. There was the same fanaticism in the crowd as Glasgow but twice as many people packed into the arena. It was somehow, impossibly, more intense. There were women dozens deep around the pits.

Ritchie absorbed the league racing before his second half rides. It was a lovely, racing track. White City had long straights, but tightish turns. West Ham was the longest circuit he had experienced apart from Claremont, Perth, where he felt he had grown up and matured as a rider.

He admired the swooping, daring style of their Australian number one, Jacko

Rintzen. Ritchie had heard about him, naturally, around the speedways, and his run of rotten luck. Christ, the bloke went quickly.

He also had a word for Ritchie.

"Heard you got Claremont weighed up," he said.

"Loved it," replied Ritchie. "But this looks my kind of place too."

"There's a slight reverse camber on the outside of the third turn," said Jacko. "If you drift too far you're left hanging out to dry."

Ritchie felt admiration and respect for Jacko. The bloke was a superstar but still found time for him, a stranger in town. Rintzen was unusual among speedmen. He wasn't full of himself, and everyone seemed to get along with him. There were famous vendettas and feuds between cinderfellas. Ritchie knew he had a couple of rivals 'hunting' for him. But Rintzen seemed to have the universal regard of all his contemporaries.

Ritchie raced to two second places in his outings, to a respectful reception from the heaving crowd. He felt he could have done better; he was a little undergeared. Hardly any of his track cronies in Scotland knew much about West Ham or how to handle it. Joe Lowther had never even seen it.

On leaving the dressing rooms Richie was overwhelmed by girl fans. Two forced their way into his wagon and performed double lovebites on him all the way up the Beckton bypass.

He felt he was back in his own lusty world again. Lovely, fragrant Morag would have been shocked beyond words by such behaviour.

Maybe he wasn't cut out for high class females after all.

WILY WEST HAM boss Vic Gordon had not invited Ritchie to the East End to reawaken his old sexual preferences

The Hammers had fought their way through to the National Trophy Final, speedway's equivalent of the FA Cup Final, but had been hit by injuries to two key team members, who would not be able to ride in the home and away legs against powerful Belle Vue (Manchester).

There was considerable prestige – and big business – in winning the trophy. Gordon had to be ready to gamble to strengthen his team for the Final. That's why he had a quiet look at this brash Scottish guy who had been blowing them all away in the Second Division for Glasgow Tigers.

Ritchie's London lovebites still had not faded under his tartan scarf when boss

Iain Harman called him to his office and said: "West Ham want to buy you right away, in time for the National Trophy Final.

"It's an offer we can't refuse."

CHAPTER 16

FROM Birdsville to Charlotte Waters, in the very heart of Australia, the landscape is thick with turpentine bushes, termite mounds and deceptive clumps of spinifex. This brittle grass is like shards of barbed wire; scratches from it leave festering sores.

Jacko was relieved he had chosen to undertake his own personal walkabout by wagon. It would have been tough on a horse in this country. Besides, he was determined not to become too attached to any horse again. Or to anyone.

Jacko had switched off intentionally on his return to Australia. An ingrained loner from childhood he needed time on his own. And a man can sure find solitude in the Australian outback.

He had been greeted and feted like a hero on his return to Baranga. Even Kerslake seemed genuinely pleased to see him and invited him to share a beer on the verandah, his holy of holies.

The hands had listened wide-eyed to his stories of West Ham, Wembley, and Belle Vue (Manchester) with its elephant, dunnies with silver taps and white-tiled walls, restaurants with little dead fish on toast, wild women with names like Glenys the Menace and red-cheeked Dutch dancing girls in clogs but not a stitch of clothing.

They guffawed coarsely at the antics of daft dirt track riders who stuffed fish on the manifolds of cars, sent empty coffins to bosses they didn't like, and seriously singed scrotums trying to fire a fart. They did not believe a bloke could share a bath with six other mates.

And they could not believe a bloke could earn five gee in six months riding a bike around in circles. Bloody ridiculous.

"Jeez, Jacko, you've lived high on the hog," they agreed. "Damned if you're not one lucky fella."

Weighing up his life to date in the brutal solitude of scrub country, Jacko had to agree they were dead right.

He was truly lucky.

Sure, he had been bowled over by bad luck. Wicked, some would say. True, he would never get over Fan and the shockingly unfair sequence of events which had split them, apparently forever. Too right there would always be a place in his heart for dear departed four-legged friends. But his life in speedway racing had worked out better than anything he had imagined in his wildest daydream.

It had given him escape. It had supplied excitement, laughter, cameraderie and, fleetingly, love. In generous helpings.

Jacko discovered he was not obsessed by status, winning or driven by an over-powering desire to be world champion. That would be terrific for the wonderful working-class fans at West Ham. But he realised it wasn't a fanatical fixation.

He was perfectly happy doing precisely what he was doing. His captain at West Ham, more widely read than most riders, had heard an adage: Live the life you love and love the life you live.

Jacko thought that was just about right.

West Ham were paying him a retainer just to return for the 1949 season.

Jacko abruptly ended this introspection.

He was ready to go.

Go back home to the Hammers, he thought ruefully.

Nearly four years after the war, Jacko returned to a Britain where speedway was still one of the only bright daubs of colour on a grey, still-austere canvas.

The milk allowance had been cut again, sugar was down to eight ounces a week, petrol had risen to two shillings and threepence a gallon.

But Jacko was getting paid just to show up at West Ham every Tuesday.

The Whacko, Jacko's Back-o – Again billboards were up all over East London.

Jacko was relaxed, and winning races. He believed he had the best workshop and mechanical set-up in London. The West Ham management attended to every need; the fans idolised him.

Cracked it, thought Jacko. Maybe I should start living the sort of life the hands back at the cattle station believe I should be living. He wanted to impress them even more.

Jacko realised with a jolt that in his sixth year in Britain he had never had his own home. Some of the time he hadn't even had his own bed. He'd been ever a lodger, a guest in other people's homes. A cuckoo.

He wanted roots but not conventionally. He wasn't sure what the answer was but stumbled on one thanks to an unexpected dalliance with a dazzling but dim Pinewood Studios starlet called Geraldine 'Jinxy' Joynson.

Jinxy, daughter of an affluent Home Counties Conservative Member of Parliament, had been the most attractive and well-developed pupil at her all-girls boarding school and the object of much admiration and attention in the showers and after lights out in the dorm.

She had become very fond of this attention and found herself responding wholeheartedly.

When, inevitably, she was snapped up for movie stardom, she found the gropings and expectations of cigar-chomping male studio executives – who somehow reminded her of toads – much to her distaste and returned to her former schoolgirl pleasures. Rumours and reports were circulating in the cinema scandal sheets so the studio publicity men were summoned from on high to stop the rot. Anyhow.

A good-old fashioned manufactured romance was called for.

West Ham boss Vic Gordon had many contacts in the British film business. He often loaned his American Oldsmobile for location work. It was no big deal to him when a Elstree chum called and said: "How would you feel if your eligible heartthrob superhero escorted Jinxy Joynson at the Film Awards Presentations at the Dorchester?" He had seen Jacko performing his tricks on the set of "Once A Jolly Swagman" and had been impressed.

Great publicity, thought Vic. As long as the boy didn't go mad and get married. He had been thinking Jacko needed some kind of involvement or folk would be thinking there was something camp about him.

Good yarn for the blokes back in Aussie, thought Jacko, when his tuxedo from Moss Bros in Covent Garden was delivered. He'd never worn a black tie before.

Pathe News, its famous trademark white cockerel crowing noisily, heralded the arrival of Jinxy and Jacko, amid flashbulbs, onto the red carpet in London's Park Lane.

The perpetually surprised Pathe commentator trilled: "Who's the new man on the arm of glamorous Pinewood starlet Jinxy Joyson as she arrives for filmland's big night at the Dorchester?

"We can tell you its speedway superstar Jacko Rintzen and whaddya know, he's brought his own girl fans and they don't seem to think much of lovely Jinxy.

"But my word, don't they make a lovely couple?"

Jinxy obligingly threw her arms around Jacko for the scrum of cameramen. She had been well schooled at Pinewood and knew the routine. Jacko identified his speedway camera chum Wilf Eden shoving among the snappers and made sure he got an exclusive angle.

They swept into the exquisitely elegant Long Room of one of the world's great hotels. Jacko absorbed the splendour and thought: This is a tale for the boys.

This really is the life.

CHAPTER 17

TO HIS considerable surprise, Jacko discovered Elstree Studios had booked adjoining rooms for them both. He had expected Vic Gordon to convey him back to Essex after all the glitter, gushing and gin-swilling.

It was a magnificently impressive room, overlooking Park Lane and away over Hyde Park. The grandeur of the bed and bathroom the boys back home could never imagine. Jacko realised that after a lifetime of monastic penitence, he was beginning to appreciate the luxury side of living. Getting a taste for it.

Jinxy floated in like a ghost in something flimsy, quietly closing the adjoining door.

She was truly lovely. But Jacko was still haunted by images of Diana Harris and the hatred on Fan's face. He had no intention of being wracked with guilt over another snatched liaison. He also realised Jinxy was just a lonely, rather frightened little girl. So they simply shared a bed, Jinxy curled like a teddy bear against Jacko's sinewy frame.

He still felt uncomfortably guilty in the morning, when they lay together in awkward silence. He wanted to escape.

He recalled, with a knot of pain in his intestines, how these had been such special moments with Fan, how they talked about anything, everything, from Baranga to

Nebraska and even, hopelessly, a future together.

Jinxy, the object of a million filmgoers fantasies, appeared to have the intelligence of an average kookaburra.

Jacko tolerated the ditsy conversation but when she observed his war wounds – again, memories of Fan's tenderness – and said: "Oh, I know a lovely make-up boy at Elstree who could powder them for you" then Jacko knew he had to get away.

Pulling on his dress shirt and trousers, he crossed Park Lane on a soft spring morning into Hyde Park, immediately drawn to a group of riders and four absolutely immaculate horses.

He had not realised many of England's elite country set, with town residences in Belgravia and Kensington, used Hyde Park for a cheerful early morning trot for their mounts, kept stabled at an astronomical cost, around Horse Guards Parade.

Elegant and haughty, the riders looked like they may have attended some glitzy dinner at the Dorchester the previous evening. One, amazingly blue-eyed, classically staturesque in the saddle, became aware of Jacko's interest and rapport with the horses.

She did not seem in the least bit fazed to encounter anyone so unconventionally dressed at that time of the morning.

"They're in top condition," he said, knuckling a wither. "Real beauties."

"You ride, then," she asked, all cut crystal.

"Used to. Not much now. At least not horses. Never thought I'd see thoroughbreds right in the middle of London. Interesting saddle, too. Never really seen one like that. No pommel to speak of."

"They're for dressage."

Jacko had heard of this highly disciplined form of equestrianism but never seen it. A bit like The Trots, he had thought. He watched for several minutes as horse and rider performed delicate trotting motions. Like slow motion, thought Jacko.

"That's some horse," he said. "And you're quite a rider."

"Where did you learn about saddles? You sound like you're a cowboy. American?"

"Not quite. Australian. Drover. Ridden a few, but never one like that."

"Maybe you would like a spin on Henry then. I don't usually allow others to ride him, particularly total strangers. It will add to your experience. And to his. He's never had an Australian drover on board. I'm Charlotte Willowby, by the way."

She did not say she was a Lady, a former debutante, and an international equestrienne. But Jacko didn't mention he was mobbed five times a week by frenzied speedway fans.

Both Charlotte and Henry swiftly recognised Jacko was a horseman of exceptional skill. Classically disciplined, the horse responded to Jacko's feathery, but firm touches. Charlotte could see Jacko's sheer pleasure on being on a horse again.

"My golly, you have ridden before," she said. "Have you ever tried show jumping? We've never seen a drover at Olympia. What a hoot.

"Daddy would love to meet you, I'm sure. He loved the Australians at Gallipoli. But what are you doing dressed like that in Hyde Park?"

"Spent the night at the Dorchester."

"Gosh, an Australian at the Dorchester. Daddy would be shocked. He said you were all incurable villains. Must fly. But maybe I'll see you again. I'm up at the Dorchester myself next weekend. Dressage Society Dinner. Henry seemed to like you, too. Chin chin"

Jacko had been so absorbed in the horses he had not noticed a photographer lurking unobtrusively in the background. The popular Press was beginning to work up a head of steam after the war. Society columns, growing in impact and influence, learned there were salacious gems to be discovered at crazy times of the day in the heart of London's West End.

Like a hooray in a dress shirt on horseback in Hyde Park at 7.30 in the morning. With a classy-looking young milady apparently encouraging him.

When the snatched pictures landed on a Fleet Street news desk, it was only a moment before a sub editor cried: "Hang on, isn't that dawn rider the same bloke that squired Jinxy Joynson to the Dorchester. And by Christ, that's Lady Charlotte Willowby, direct from the Horse of the Year Show and filthy rich Daddy's Sussex estate."

Vic Gordon nearly fell out of his chair when he saw the page lead. Speed Ace Jacko In Sexy Double, screamed the banner headline.

"Speedway superstar Jacko Rintzen, idol of East End female fans, conquered the West End yesterday in the company of two of England's most lusted after females in less than twenty four hours. Rintzen, a former cattle hand from the Australian outback, was the envy of every red-blooded man in the land when he was gorgeous film star Jinxy Joynson's date for The British Film Awards at the Dorchester. But now it can be revealed, only a few hours later, he was seen hobnobbing with Lady Charlotte Willowby, wealthy darling of the county set, on horse back in Hyde Park while still in evening dress! Rintzen, who earns over £100 a week and is rated one of the strong favourites for the revised World Speedway Championship later this year, will be back in a more familiar saddle tomorrow evening riding for his club West Ham against Harringay. Jinxy Joynson's reaction to her dashing boyfriend riding away from home in Hyde Park is not known!"

145

Vic Gordon shook his head. The boy had one girl friend in two years and now was involved with two of England's ritziest females inside twenty four hours. He's bigger news than the end of the Berlin Airlift!

Bloody terrific for box office business, though.

THE LURE of high living and high society hobnobbing attracted Jacko back to the Dorchester the following weekend. He wanted to live life to the ultimate.

He was tickled by the idea of riding a true thoroughbred right in the heart of the British Empire. The horse, he thought wryly, not Lady Charlotte. He wondered if she would show up in Hyde Park, and her reaction to the lurid headlines.

His wicked mates in the dressing room at West Ham had stuck a big photo of Errol Flynn by his peg on the wall.

Almost automatically, he booked himself into the Dorchester. He relished the room overlooking Hyde Park, the hustle of Park Lane and the simply sensational fuss the hotel made of their guests.

Lady Charlotte had actually left a message for him at reception. "You dog. You didn't tell me you were a STAR. Now all my friends want to meet you. Much impressed by headlines in scandal rags. I'll be in the Long Room bar after the bash."

Jacko extended his stay at the hotel. Charlotte went with him for supper in the Long Room. A sepia-skinned pianist tinkled Gershwin in the background.

Surely this is as far from the bunkhouse floor at Baranga as it is humanly possible to go, thought Jacko. He again extended his stay. Money was not a problem. He could earn enough for an overnight room in just over sixty seconds of track action. The hotel were delighted to accommodate a guest who attracted media attention.

So Jacko, who had slept on floors with Lascar seamen and in straw with sick horses and groggy greyhounds, gradually, almost accidently, drifted into the rarified atmosphere and glittering company of one of the world's greatest hotels. Chambermaids vied to change his bed, competed to serve early morning tea. The chef, a surprise speedway enthusiast, learned about Jacko's inborn aversion to meat so concocted specials just for him; something called a soufflé, scrambled eggs and smoked salmon for breakfast, wondrous omelettes.

Barmen learned Jacko was no beer drinker but would take a light, chilled glass of wine. They kept a corner bar stool for him.

The head doorman, who seemed to know everything about the West End and was on nodding terms with royalty, introduced him to a cabbie, Taxi Trev from Tottenham, a speedway nut, who just wanted to watch racing every evening.He was delighted to ferry Jacko to meetings.

So Chinners conveyed Jacko's machines to tracks and Trev drove Jacko to speedway by taxi: east up the Commercial Road through Mile End to West Ham; north via the Edgware Road to Wembley and Harringay; over the river past Kennington Oval and Clapham Common to Wimbledon; down the Elephant and Castle to the Old Kent Road to New Cross. The arrangement suited Jacko down to the ground. He was wary driving on London's rushing streets and avenues. Speedway he could handle; Hyde Park Corner at five o'clock rush hour was a different proposition.

Trev was delighted to drive for petrol money, stay, watch the meetings, then talk non-stop about them as he ran Jacko back to the Dorchester.

It was an unique life. Jacko was not quite sure how he had stumbled into it. He wanted it to last

It was quite a story.

But the busybody Fleet Street fraternity were beaten to the exclusive by an enthusiastic kid in his first year as a cub reporter on the Birmingham Post.

IN ITS TWENTY-FIRST season, British speedway was booming as heartily as ever in 1949.

There were thirty-three clubs spread over three healthy divisions, more millions than ever attending. Although London remained the El Dorado of the Cinderfellas, the Midlands was emerging steadily as a rival power base. Seven Midland tracks operated across the divisions, with Birmingham, promoted that year into the First Division, as their frenetic standard bearer

West Ham, with Jacko running sweetly now at number one, had to visit the pacy 402-yard Perry Barr circuit, home of Birchfield Harriers AC, an arena almost unrivalled for sheer fan frenzy. Brum was speedway mad.

Senior speedway had not taken Jacko to the Midlands much previously. The fans were turning somersaults to see him, so on the night before, Jacko accepted a big money booking for an individual meeting at nearby Second Division track Coventry, which had opened the year before.

He was curious to appear there: dressing room and pits gossip insisted the promoter, Charles Appletree, was the best organised bloke on the planet.

Jacko was stunned when he arrived at the purpose-built stadium at Brandon, six miles from the city centre, to discover his own allocated car parking and pit space and even his own personally monogrammed towels in the showers. This was The Dorchester Hotel of speedway.

The meeting, on a smooth, slickish surface that Jacko relished, ran like clockwork.

All the riders were unanimous about the boss. "That bloke could organise chaos," they said.

Birmingham will have to be very special to match this, thought Jacko.

But it was.

With a stadium capacity of 30,000, fans were literally fighting to get in. Queues formed six hours before racing. Police were needed on each turnstile. Thousands who were unable to gain admittance milled about outside the stadium, listening to the race results echoing from the tannoy system, cheering wildly at a spectacle they couldn't see.

Wedged solidly inside, the partisan home crowd crackled with enough electricity to power the entire Midlands motor industry.

The Brummies, with huge red 'B's on their yellow breastplates, had their own Australian wonderboy, dubbed the Blond Bombshell. He had been a postal worker down Sydney way, a post-war overnight sensation. Jacko had appeared with him previously in Australian Test teams and knew full well he was a talented, showy performer.

Birmingham's hordes worshipped him because he played to the gallery, winning races on his back wheel, playing with the opposition. Without question, he was a handful.

Too good for Jacko when they first met. His local track knowledge zipped him past Jacko on the outside down the back straight and, with the crowd baying, he held off Jacko inside and out to win.

Next time they met, Jacko knew where he'd be attacking, moved line, and carefully closed down the gap on the outside.

This time he held on for the chequered flag as the crowd's cheers died stillborn.

Honours even. Ay up, but gri-ate speedway, agreed the thousands as they filed out to their grimy industrial estates and Mitchell & Butler's best bitter.

In the dressing room after racing – no monogrammed towels here – Jacko was approached by a very polite young man who said his name was John Shapland. He was the speedway correspondent for the local paper. He had recently achieved his first by-line with an at-home piece with the Blond Bombshell and was bursting keen to get another.

Could he do a similar piece with Australia's other speedway sensation?

Jacko secretly enjoyed talking to pressmen. He loved their bonhomie and bullshine. And while he had been in the pits before racing began, he had squatted on his haunches and read a piece in the Birmingham speedway programme by Shapland, with which he completely empathised.

Shapland had written:

"My heart was lost to speedway racing at precisely 6.30pm on the night of Saturday July 6, 1946 at Alexander Sports Stadium, Perry Barr, Birmingham. The Brummies beat Sheffield by two points in an ACU Cup match. It was love at first sight. She was eighteen, I was only fifteen. But I was infatuated utterly, captivated totally."

Jacko thought: "Reckon that sums up exactly how I felt about speedway. Love at first sight."

"Not a problem," he replied to Shapland. "Although I don't know how you'll handle the 'at-home' angle. These days I'm sort of living at the Dorchester."

He could not help but notice that Shapland's jaw seemed to drop open.

SHAPLAND'S exclusive was syndicated to newspapers worldwide. It splashed all over Australia.

Greatest Rags To Riches Story Ever

Speedway star Jacko Rintzen, one-time saddletramp from the back end of nowhere, now resides among royalty and the super-rich at the Dorchester, the world's most elegant hotel.

Rintzen, who worked his passage from the Australian outback to Britain on a ramshackle freighter and slept in sack-cloth and straw, now has silken sheets and servants dishing up smoked salmon.

Idol of the West Ham thousands, Rintzen even travels to London speedway tracks by London taxi and keeps the meter ticking before returning for a light late supper in high West End society company.

From Aussie stumblebum to Burlington Bertie in three years, Rintzen, 29, is a former cattle ranch jackaroo who now exercises thoroughbred horses with the county set in Hyde Park and regularly escorts former Deb of the Year, Lady Charlotte Willowby. Her opinion of Jacko: "He's a brilliant horseman and an absolute baa-lamb."

He was introduced to the luxury of the Dorchester by glamourgirl Pinewood starlet

149

Geraldine 'Jinxy' Joynson, who recently won acclaim for her vivid portrayal of an intimidated girl prisoner in the hit film Forbidden Lusts.

Rintzen, who last year earned over £5000 in prize money, was twice robbed of the British Championship by injury but is one of the favourites for the first official World Championship to be staged since 1938 at Wembley in September.

He says: "I've never had a home of my own and I never imagined anything like the Dorchester. It's not what I'm used to. But I've kind of grown into it now. It suits me fine."

A spokesman for the Dorchester said: "We are delighted to accommodate Mr Rintzen. He is a gentleman and well respected by our staff and guests."

If Rintzen does win speedway's World Championship in September and claim his place among the sport's immortals, expect the party of the year in Park Lane.

The Cinderfella sport will be having a ball!

The follow-ups were furious. *Picture Post* had four pages of photographs, with Jacko being served tea in bed on a silver tray and a footman holding open the door of Trev's taxi.

Pathe News were back with another item. The still surprised commentator gushed: "Remember we showed Jacko's introduction to the Dorchester with Jinxy Joynson? Well, well, it looks like he's taking over the place!"

Jacko even got a cable from Kerslake back at Baranga: Dear Stumblebum. Stop. Always knew you'd come good. Stop. The boys say will you bring one of those starlet sheilas back for them. Stop. Stay safe. Kerslake.

The thriving speedway press continually held their front pages for the most recent Rintzen activity.

Vic Gordon and the West Ham speedway management were over the moon with all the media attention. Jacko was getting as much coverage as Gorgeous Gussie and her frilly knickers at Wimbledon tennis.

But Vic had a quiet word with Jacko: "Don't forget we pay you to race, not to rave it up."

MAYBE it was word from Kerslake that fired Jacko's conscience. He discovered he was continually recalling that sizzling sunset on the verandah, their unexpectedly deep conversation.

Kerslake revealing his surprising, but complete love for an Aboriginal maiden called Mali.

His bitter words kept returning to Jacko: "Thousands of bloody nights regretting I gave up trying to find her."

Jacko, with the world at his feet, still could not get Fan Harris out of his mind. Hadn't he given her up too easily? Hadn't he been the complete drongo to just give up without a fight? Did he walk away much too easily? Wasn't she worth it? Wasn't she worth even giving up speedway? Surely she wasn't as devastated as she had seemed? Surely time would have eased the pain?

He thought, he knew, they had so much going for them.

He visualised himself like Kerslake, brooding beerily for decades, choked by regret.

He had to find Fan. He would not give up this way.

As anonymously as possible, with hat pulled down and coat collars up, Jacko drove nervously past imposing Upton Park, home of West Ham Utd FC, along Green Street.

The florist shop, scene of Jacko's shame and life-changing downfall, was deserted, boarded up, with drooping For Sale notices hanging drunkenly. The very sight of the place filled Jacko with revulsion. Why didn't I shove the old girl away, like I have with so many Track Spares, he thought. What a pelican I was.

Jacko had a Plan B.

He knew where Fan worked. He had dropped her at her office a couple of times after those weekends which now were such a distant, bittersweet memory.

He wanted to go in Fan's footsteps. There seemed to be something daftly poetic about that. So he boarded a District Line tube train and rattled along the same route that Fan had travelled, hunched up in his overcoat for there were still West Ham Speedway posters with his effigy plastered over every station. Jacko did not want to be recognised. This had to be a solitary pilgrimage.

He knew he needed to alight at Chancery Lane. Opposite the station there was an attractive row of Dickensian type cottage fronts, a two hundred yard stroll up Gray's Inn Road, a left turn into Theobalds Road. Jacko found Fan's old office on the corner of Jockey's Fields and wondered again about the origin of so many street names in the heart of London.

He walked straight and asked for Miss Ann Harris.

The receptionist hardly looked up.

"She left some time ago," she said, a bit sniffy.

"D'you know where she went?"

"No, abroad I think. Her Mum died or something."

"Sorry to keep going on, but is there somebody who does have some idea where she is? Did she have a friend she still contacts? It's quite important to me."

Jacko suddenly realised he had been nurturing wild thoughts that Fan would come bounding down the stairs into reception, showing her great teeth.

The receptionist looked irritated. "I don't really know. She's been gone some time. Who are you, anyway?"

"Oh, just a very old friend who hasn't seen her in some time. It really is important."

"Just a moment, then. I'll ring Andrew Sommerville. She worked with him. Maybe he can help. Is there a name I can give them?"

"Nah, just say it's a friend."

Jacko sat in a corner, while the receptionist turned away and buried her chin in a telephone. She looked suspiciously across at Jacko a couple of times.

"Mr Sommerville is busy, can't spare any time," she said. "But he's sending down Jessica Braithwaite. She was friendly with Fan when she was here. They used to lunch together."

Nervously, Jacko wondered where the Poms dug up their names before a business-like, reed-slender girl in a two-piece suit with an ankle-length skirt, with tied-back hair and rimless glasses, walked across to him, looking inquisitive.

Her first words hit Jacko like a kick in the guts from a healthy carthorse.

"You're Jacko," she said. The same first words that Fan had said to him.

But Jessica was refreshingly sympathetic.

Jacko had feared she might scream at him that he was the bastard who had wrecked her friend's life and kick his ass.

But she spoke gently, in short, stunted sentences, like she was transcribing a shorthand note.

Fan had been wrecked when her mother had died. She had just said she had died in a car accident. She didn't say anything else. Jessica thought there might be more to it. Fan's Mum had a terrible reputation.

Fan had been determined to get away from the East End. She had said that with her mother gone, there was nothing left to keep her there. She wanted to travel, forget about everything.

She had mentioned Jacko, said he was her boyfriend, different to all the other ones, big name in speedway or something. Jessica had mentioned him to her kid brother and he'd been very impressed. But Fan said it wasn't really serious. Best to make a clean break.

She hadn't really returned to the office. Bloody Mr Sommerville had been very offish with her for weeks. She found a job as a secretary at the new NATO headquarters in Paris and had an attic flat somewhere along the Seine.

Yes, she had written a few times. She was loving Paris and her new job. She was apparently working for some high flying American Major General from Kentucky, an expert in logistics or some such. They were getting on fine. Almost sure they were shacked up together. He had promised to take her to the States to meet his folks. Enormously wealthy and influential. Fan seemed to have forgotten totally about the East End and her life here. She said she had no intention ever of returning.

Jessica smiled brightly. "Is that helpful? I'll tell her you called if she writes again."

"Aw, best not to bother," said Jacko. "Best not to remind her of the past now that she seems to be so well set. But thanks for your time."

"Fine, if that's what you want. Oh, do you think you could sign my notebook to Charlie?"

The street looked grey and so did the world as Jacko trudged back down the Gray's Inn Road. Damn fool, he told himself, expecting her to come bounding down with her very special, unforgettable smile.

He thought Kerslake would probably go galloping down the Champs d'Elysees with his two-bore and challenge this glamorous American to a shoot-out.

But Fan seemed to have found all she had ever wanted. She had dreamed of America and her dreams were coming true. In Kentucky. Hadn't he read they had blue grass there? Jacko couldn't picture that.

Jacko decided to walk, lost in thought, down High Holborn, across Shaftesbury Circus, where the neon signs were winking out the reawakening entertainment in the West End, a long trek down bustling Oxford Street, to Park Lane. The uniformed doorman at the Dorchester greeted him effusively. "What a pleasure to see you, sir."

Well, at least I know Fan's happy, thought Jacko.

And I've made a little boy called Charlie happy, just by signing a dog-eared short-hand notebook.

It was time to return to his first love.

Speedway racing.

CHAPTER 18

VINCENTIUS VITTORIO VOLTORI leaned gloomily on the bar of the Lucky Chip saloon of the Flamingo Casino Resort in the astonishing, Gold Rush-style emerging post-war desert settlement called Las Vegas.

He had even missed out on the complimentary Michelob circulated by scantily-clad Flamingo waitresses in pink fishnet stockings and suspenders.

"Buy me a beer, Lana," he said to his slender, hard-faced but modestly stylish companion.

"For chrissake, V-Man, don't say you're busted already."

With his initials, Vincente had been known as V-Man since his first year in high school on the mean streets back of the Hoboken waterfront.

Lana's irritated voice betrayed the flattish vowels of the more northerly states of the USA. Word was she had migrated south to Nevada with the original pioneering Chicago gaming mob and had even been a squeeze of Ben 'Bugsy' Siegel, who had been gunned down in Beverly Hills soon after opening this Flamingo complex. She had been around.

Now she earned her poky casino staff suite either as, in Vegas-speak, a 'niece'(escorting very old men who ought to know better around the casino) or a 'shill'(making up the number or sitting in on a card school, encouraging punters to lose their money).

She had done other things to get by but now was bankrolling the Hollywood-handsome but idiotically irresponsible Vincente the V-Man, a decade her junior.

"Busted, cleaned out, a broken man, a bum," he replied, with grave drama. "Tomorrow, the soup queues. Ah Lana, can you spare a dime?"

"You're absolutely impossible. It's high time you settled down in your rich Daddy's business. I'm sick of picking up your tabs."

"I am far too young and good looking to waste my life in the catering business. My number is about to come up. I'm about to roll, about to strike the Mother Lode."

A bartender with slicked-back hair and snake eyes who resembled George Raft, answered a telephone, looked up and said: "You Voltori? Long distance call from London, England, for you"

Mystified, V-Man grabbed the phone and said: "This is Voltori. Who's this?"

A booming voice echoed down the line: "This is Freddy Mountford from New Cross Speedway in London."

"Well, I'll be Goddamned," said the V-Man. "What did they do with the Old Cross?"

DESPERATE AND DESTITUTE, V-Man's father Vittorio Voltori had somehow managed to wangle a last-minute stowage passage on the SS Capri Packet out of the fetid, poverty-wracked docks of post World War I Naples, bound for the New World, a fresh, hopeful beginning.

Heaving about in the hold during the exhausting voyage he had quite literally stumbled across another down-and-out, penniless emigrant from the Naples slums, Maria Tarni. Theirs was hardly a romance. Two lost souls, they clung together for support.

After checking through Ellis Island, under the Statue of Liberty, a devastated Maria told Vittorio she feared she was pregnant and must immediately seek a priest to confess. They left the rickety bus together at the first immigrant Italian reception centre in Hoboken, New York.

They had exchanged one derelict dockland dump for another.

Vittorio wanted to hit on, find fortune in this brave New World. But Maria wanted to hang on to the hems of her priest's robes on the dockside streets.

Teresa Maria was born seven months later. A son, christened Vincentius (from the original Latin) Vittorio arrived nearly five years later.

By the time his son was born, Vittorio had hardly found the fortune he had been seeking in this so-called land of opportunity. He was breadlining by, living in a coldwater tenement, just about feeding his young family, sweating in the kitchen of a dockside diner, washing dishes, cleaning grease pans, occasionally serving as a short order waiter.

But Vittorio knew there was no way his family would starve.

He could always go to his old Neapolitan 'Families' for assistance and aid. The Italian immigrants had imported their own unique social structure and code of justice to the USA with them.

Unexpectedly, the 'Families' changed Voltori's fortunes.

The mob with oldtime Neapolitan links regularly used the dockside diner. It was part of their territory. Vittorio sometimes served them. One night a rival outfit from uptown were clearly waiting in ambush. Vittorio managed to sneak away to warn his former hometown contacts. There had been a showdown, a shootout, one of many in those years. Thanks to the pre-alert, the Neapolitans had prevailed.

They were grateful to Vittorio. So grateful they warned off the owner of the diner and gave the business to Vittorio. In return, he did small "services". With the 'Family' behind him, Vittorio prospered. His family began to enjoy three meals a day.

Teresa, dark, voluptuous but devout, grew up close to her mother, like her mother. She was a good girl, with old fashioned, old world values.

Young Vincente was exactly the opposite: brash, arrogant, rebellious, streetwise, classically Latino handsome, he was a wild child of the New World, causing his parents anguish and despair.

He ducked school to roam dockland, played street baseball (excelling as a first baseman over a steaming drain), ran with the gangs, chased and nearly always kissed the girls. He was a tearaway. But with charm and a winning smile. Which did not always get him out of trouble.

He spent time in a Young Offenders Institute after clobbering a rival gang member with a baseball bat for insulting his sister Teresa. He'd been apprehended carrying illicit liquor, had brushes with the Narcotics Squad. Vittorio had to call on the influences of the Neapolitan 'Family' to help him beat more than one rap.

"What are we gonna do with you, Vincente?" pleaded Vittorio. "You will drive Mama into an early grave. Why don't you take more interest in the family business? Why can't you be good like your sister?"

"Because I want to have fun, Popsy" he replied with that disarming grin. He always called his father "Popsy", which irritated Vittorio enormously. Italian kids were supposed to respect their elders.

So Vittorio was quietly relieved when the Neapolitan 'Family' indicated they wished him and his family to move on. There was a new role for him. That suited Vittorio. He was keen to get V-Man, as everyone now called him, away from New York. He had been flirting dangerously with the mob. Vittorio had nightmares about finding the bullet-ridden corpse of his only son in some gutter.

The Voltori's were relocated to a much more updated diner on the freeway outside San Diego, right on the California-Mexico border. Fast food was catching on rapidly, business was expanding. The 'Families' needed a staging post right on the border. Mysterious, silent figures in fedoras, up from Mexico or Baja California, regularly left unmarked packages in plain wrapping at Voltori's Diner, to be collected later by other mysterious, uncommunicative figures.

Nobody asked questions. Vittorio learned that way back.

Besides, he had hit on an unexpected winner. He had noticed the North American passion for having a glass of water before dining, particularly in the desert temperatures of San Diego. Vittorio, with his usual untraceable backers, started to market bottled water. The mob had cornered the market in olive oil. Why not water, too? It was like gold dust in the desert, where truly amazing expansion was erupting. The workforce on the Hoover Dam couldn't get enough.

Vittorio grew quite wealthy. As World War Two progressed he had military contracts to supply water. Island-hopping GIs would kill for it. Vittorio was desperate for his son to take an interest, take over the burgeoning business. But the V-Man had found another obsessive distraction.

The Voltori's freeway fast food joint was a regular stop-off for a gang of bikers who called themselves The Sandblasters. Every weekend they roared out into the wastes of the 13,500 square mile Mojave Desert for wild, rip-it-up joyriding sessions. They had Harleys, Indians, Peashooters, they called them "sickles" and the V-Man was captivated. Initially he went sandblasting riding pillion. But he was soon raising dust clouds riding solo on borrowed bikes.

Vittorio shelled up the dollars to buy his own Indian twin cycle. Anything to keep the V-Man off the streets, associating with characters who made sweaty, leatherclad bikers seem respectable. V-Man was becoming one of the most daring Sandblasters when he could not duck the draft any more. He served out the tailend of World War II in Europe. Vittorio used his influence to ensure his son would not have to dodge too many bullets. V-Man strolled through his time in the Service Corps, never fired a bullet in anger, saw only German PoWs and one of the last Messerschmitt 109s in Normandy skies while wickedly working his way through a willing line of mademoiselles, drinking plenty of vino, smooching to Glenn Miller.

After riotous victory celebrations, V-Man shipped back home still riproaring restless, determined not to get locked into Popsy's damned business. His old Indian sickle soon burst back into life as V-Man escaped the dreary day-to-day civilian routine, out with a new brigade of Sandblasters.

Who had discovered another mode of motor cycle mayhem.

They called it speedway.

V-Man learned Californian dirt trackers had hit the genuine bigtime in Britain before the war. A pioneer called Sprouts Elder had, like him, actually ridden a specially adapted Indian machine and trousered thousands of dollars. US riders had finished 1-2-3 in the World Speedway Championship Final at Wembley, London in 1937.

Now post-war speedway in London was reported to be bigger than the World Series, better dame-bait and more sensational than even Sinatra.

It was simple enough for the Sandblasters to carve out their own speedway in the wide open Mojave. Broadsiding came naturally to the V-Man. He loved the cut and thrust, the competitive element of limited lap racing. Humping and bumping over sand dunes seemed abstract by comparison.

The Sandblasters rode north together, like an old Wild West possee, up to Los Angeles, to see a proper speedway meeting for themselves at a track called Lincoln Park. It was fringed by palm trees but little more than a desert circuit enclosed by prefabricated bench seating. Bleachers they called them.

V-Man immediately loved the sight, the sound, the Goddam smell of it.

He learned anyone could take a bike, try to be quick enough to qualify for beginner races. After one disappointing attempt on his aging Indian, he knew he must obtain a proper speedway machine. Vittorio agreed to buy him one – with a condition. He was getting growing orders for water from this crazy development right out in the desert involving the 'Families' called Las Vegas, where it was stinking hot.

V-Man could go amuse himself at this speedway if he agreed to look after his water business in Vegas.

A machine was obtained from a weary looking pre-war rider who looked like Mickey Rooney and had ridden at somewhere called Wimbledon for a year or so. The machine was inscribed JAP but the lowscale US speedway setup, still aware of post Pearl Harbour feelings, called these bikes Prestwiches. V-Man was mightily impressed with its muscular, punch-above-its-weight performance.

The machine had wide, cow-catcher handlebars which suited V-Man's acute sense of showmanship. He practised alone for hours, deep in the desert, disturbing only the lizards. Vittorio was delighted he was keeping out of mischief.

In the restricted competition at Lincoln Park, V-Man swiftly progressed through the handicaps. He tried his hand on the unusual circuit at Santa Monica, which followed the lines of a baseball diamond, and appeared upstate at Sacramento. Soon, he was pitched in against the handful of experienced international performers who were, in truth, riding speedway for a hobby. It was no hobby for the V-Man. He wanted to win. He wanted to stand out. He had racing leathers made with the red, green and white colours of the Italian national flag painted in a 'V' from shoulders to waist. He took his audacity onto the dirt with him. He could never stay out of mischief long.

He also had to keep his end of Vittorio's bargain and look after the Las Vegas water business.

Vegas was an impossible temptation for a guy like the V-Man.

Less than half a century before a collection of huts with a population of around thirty, it did not boast a railroad until 1905. But Vegas had been one of the very few centres to thrive during the Great Depression of the 1930s with thousands of construction workers from nearby Hoover Dam inflating the local economy.

The legalisation of gambling and the liberalisation of morality and divorce laws forged the swift emergence of Las Vegas as an entertainments hotbed. Inevitably, it had attracted the 'Families'. Bugsy Siegel had pioneered the first major Casino Hotel, the Flamingo, where V-Man made his poolside headquarters.

Las Vegas was his kind of town. He relished its neon-lit brashness, its freewheeling morality, its round-the-clock, whoop-de-doo party atmosphere. Its unique outrageousness: Goddam it, they even sold seats on the roof of the Flamingo for punters to view the atomic bomb tests out in the desert!

And the V-Man was a Las Vegas sort of animal.

With his movie star, Italianate looks and smile, his sharpely cut lightweight gabardine suits, always a spotless shirt and plain, one-coloured silk tie and banded fedora, Vincentius Vittori Voltori was the archetypal louche Las Vegas lounge lizard.

Vittorio quickly realised he had made a mistake. Big mistake. His precious playboy son was gambling and partying away all the profits from his Vegas enterprise. His backers were not pleased. He had angrily ordered V-Man back to San Diego and was replacing him with a more trustworthy operative, his son in law. Teresa had married a sensible Italian boy.

On getting the recall, V-Man had reacted by roaring off on a wingding, hitting the crap tables. He was contemplating his fortunes in the Lucky Chip saloon, bumming beer from an obliging shill, when the telephone call came from New Cross Speedway. NESTLING behind the Old Kent Road, amid the costermonger cobbles, backstreet boxing gymnasiums and pubs with names like The Thomas A'Beckett, New Cross Rangers were having a funny old season.

Although in the top three of the National League, Wimbledon, their bitter South London rivals, on the bottom, were attracting bigger crowds and bolder headlines. The Dons boss Ralph Greenhalgh, quietly maintaining Transatlantic contacts, had caused a great stir by flying in the top Canadian track ace. It was regarded as a major scoop.

New Cross chief Freddy Mountford, far famed in speedway for inventing magnetic starting gates back in 1934, liked to believe he and the Rangers had exclusive links with the North American track scene.

Californian Jack Milne had been a New Cross rider when he won the World Championship in 1937. New Cross fans hollered hoarsely when he was the only rider to beat the 1938 champion on the Final night. He had been one of the favourites for the crown before World War II dimmed the speedway floodlights in 1939.

Mountford would have relished having Milne, or his younger brother Cordy (who had been third in the 1937 Final), back in the New Cross line-up after the war. But they were making a fortune in prefabricated buildings in Los Angeles, appearing locally on an occasional basis. But they kept in regular contact. Mountford believed he knew the Stateside scene better than any of his rivals.

But that damned Greenhalgh over at Wimbledon had upstaged him with this flying Canadian. Pride demanded New Cross signed somebody. Mountford had kept a Work Permit up his sleeve in case the Milnes might be tempted. He would have liked to have signed another pre-war American ace, Wilbur Lamoreaux. But he'd been drafted in to bolster the newly-promoted Birmingham side. Mountford needed to produce a rabbit from his hat. Because he knew the Lincoln Park track was similar in size to New Cross, he made a series of long distance calls to sources in California. And amazingly ended up talking to some flippant flash harry in what appeared to be a Wild West desert frontier town.

Ignoring the V-Man's opening crack, Mountford continued: "I hear you've been matching the Milnes and Lamoreaux at Lincoln Park?"

"Yup, keeping up," replied V-Man.

"Have you ever considered racing in British speedway?"

"Nope. Never."

"What would you want to fly over to ride for New Cross for the last four months of the season? You'll find the track just like Lincoln Park. It will suit your style"

V-Man had a wonderful vision of his Popsy's face if he told him he could stuff the business because he was going to England.

"Ride in England? I'll come for five thousand dollars and a loose woman."

"OK, I'll pay that. But you'll have to find your own woman. You won't have any trouble over here. There's a BOAC flight out of Los Angeles in two days. I'll book you on that."

Mountford's voice echoed as though he was speaking down a pipeline under the sea. Crazy, thought V-Man, I spent most of my Army time working on the French end of PLUTO supplying fuel to the guys roaring on over the Rhine. But that reminded him of logistics.

"What about a sickle?" he asked.

"A what?"

"A sickle. A machine. A bike."

"We'll build one for you. New Cross has the best workshops in London. You can modify it to suit yourself when you get here. I'll telegraph a contract confirming all the details. Where should I address it?"

"You must have come through the business address in San Diego to find me here. Send it there. I must go home to fetch my own handlebars. And to see the look on Popsy's face."

"We're not paying extra for handlebars. You'll have to carry them hand luggage. Oh, and don't mention you are coming to any newspapermen. I want a big surprise Press launch over here."

"Tell 'em they ain't seen nuthin' yet."

MAMA wailed, sister Teresa sobbed, Popsy raged predictably and Lana begged to go with him. But V-Man grew increasingly enthusiastic about his adventure. Five grand just to goof about on a bike. Californian speedway was little more than an amateur Sunday afternoon excursion. British speedway sounded the real thing.

He had loved what he had seen of Europe. And European women. Mainly in transit, he'd seen little of England. But he was fascinated by English femininity. He'd seen an interview with Vivien Leigh, an extremely hot potato in the States since her role in the blockbuster film Gone With The Wind. V-Man drooled at the thought of carrying her off to bed like Clark Gable. When she dropped her Scarlett O'Hara Southern Belle drawl for the interview, her cool, cultered accent was pure class.

The V-Man wanted to pluck an English rose.

Even the BOAC air hostess was a turn-on. Aloof, but cute.

Freddy Mountford, waiting at the gate at Northolt while V-Man convinced

Customs he really was carrying handlebars and not some contraband post-war weaponry, a bizarre mortar which would fire around corners, was well pleased with his acquisition.

The kid looked like Tyrone Power striding through Arrivals. He would attract screaming headlines, screaming fans. He would make Greenhalgh's Canadian look like a bank clerk.

V-Man was quietly installed in a staff bungalow at Forest Hills Golf Course, where Mountford was a shareholder and longstanding committeeman. He was ferried to the New Cross workshops, introduced to the leathery-faced chief mechanic Herb Call, who had the very latest Martin-JAP waiting for him. He sniffed at V-Man's handlebars. "Wide enough, aren't they?" he grumbled. "My Gawd, if you get in front there won't be room for anyone to go by!"

"Sounds good to me," replied V-Man. The bike was a beauty, aces high. He liked the look of the tiny New Cross track. It would sure be fun to ride. Mountford had booked the Rye House training track for a day for a secret training session. He could travel with a New Cross team mate, who even owned an American car, a Buick.

V-Man sailed around Rye House. The bike did not miss a beat. It was vastly better, quicker than anything he had ever experienced. British surfaces were grippier than the US. There were not a lot of cinders around in California. But the V-Man found drive everywhere. Just as he had thought, this was fun. The New Cross contingent watched him circulate Rye House, outgating and out manoeuvring his experienced new team mate and chauffeur. Eyebrows arched in appreciation.

Mountford had unearthed a real blockbuster.

The New Cross chief smiled like Machaivelli and declared: "We'll have a major Press Launch and introduce you into the team for our next home match.

"Pity it isn't against Wimbledon. It's West Ham."

FRENZIED HYSTERIA greeted V-Man's introduction to the Old Kent Road speedway faithful. New Cross had been going well, getting results, but the team were solid rather than spectacular. They lacked colour, pizzazz.

Vincente Voltori, with his dashing looks and colourful leathers, gave them immediate glamour. For two generations the British public had been mesmerised by the untouchable razzle dazzle of Hollywood, which this V-Man seemed to epitomise absolutely. All Americans appeared to be movie stars to most Brits.

Now New Cross at last had a genuine pin-up boy to rival the heartthrobs at West

163

Ham, Wimbledon, even Birmingham.

V-Man had never encountered anything faintly resembling crowd reaction in British speedway. In America, there was no team racing, just individual events. Non partisan, almost indifferent spectators basked on the bleachers, swilling beer, applauding politely.

In Britain the fans were completely nutty.

V-Man was mobbed by fans, mostly girls, on his twenty five yard downslope walk from the changing rooms to the New Cross pits, sited out in the open on the third and fourth turns of the tight little bowl. Enthusiasts had been queuing since two in the afternoon to get their first glimpse of this hotly ballyhooed American. Every scruffy kid seemed to shout: "Got any gum, chum." The pits were at least fifty deep right round in wild-eyed girls, smothered in orange and black New Cross colours. They looked at him as though he was of another planet. One group had a huge placard inscribed: V-Man is THE man.

He was aware there were swathes of West Ham fans in red, white and blue, frantic to upstage, intimidate the big star New Cross arrival. They were chanting "Jacko, Jacko, Jacko" monotonously. V-Man had read about this flying but unlucky Aussie with the show biz image and ritzy girl friends. He noticed his strawy thatch at the visitors end of the pits. He looked one lean, mean bozo.

New Cross exploded as V-Man leapt into the lead in his debut ride. Mechanical ace Herb Call had fitted a slightly lower gearing, figuring that V-Man, used to hugging the inside in Lincoln Park handicaps, would not stray from the inside line. With sweeping handlebars, V-Man did seem to cover all the track. He was difficult to pass. Over the chequered flag, with the Old Kent Road rocking, V-Man milked his reception. Man, this was a gas.

In his second ride he faced Jacko Rintzen.

They accelerated off the starting gate together, shoulder to shoulder. But this time the American was on the outside.

Bold V-Man still went for the inside line, in an impetuous chopping movement. Rintzen gave not a fraction. The V-Man bounced off Jacko's right shoulder, straightened momentarily, then slide off untidily into the safety fence. New Cross howled in protest, West Ham brayed in pleasure. V-Man had his first lesson in the ruthless rough and tumble of British racing.

It was not in Vincente Voltori's nature to be dumped on his butt without reaction.

After the race he strode across to Jacko's corner of the pits, with hundreds of pitside New Cross fans screaming for him to flatten the Aussie.

"Heard you were a cowhand," he said to Jacko.

164

"Drover"

"Well, listen good, cowhand. You do that to me again and you're going to have one helluva stampede to handle. I'll be gunning for you, man."

"I'll be waiting."

The pair were not programmed to meet again that night. V-Man picked up another win and a second. New Cross fanatics went home to their grey terraces very happy. The following morning the Daily Express blazed: 'Hooray for Hollywood. Voltori brings his own movie-style magic to the Old Kent Road. His signing is a big, big scoop for Freddy Mountford and New Cross."

When he eventually escaped from the fans, V-Man insisted his team-mate Laurie Franks chauffeur him to London's West End, to a famous Italian restaurant in Charlotte Street, adjacent to Tottenham Court Road.

"We'll never get a table," said Franks.

"I will," said V-Man. "I got contacts."

He gabbled away volubly in Italian at the booking desk, clearly mentioning names like Don Somebody or other and Napoli until a patriarchal figure emerged, wreathed in smiles, exclaiming: "Ben trovato, Vincente. You are welcome, welcome" and locked him in a bear-like embrace.

Wine flowed, the waiters sang a chorus from Puccini's Tosca and an endless line of Latin lovelies competed to plaster V-Man's immaculate shirt collar with vermilion lipstick smudges.

"Ain't this the life," said V-Man to his bemused team-mate. "I am falling in love with this town.

"But I've still got a score to straighten with that cowhand..."

CHAPTER 19

ROGER TREVELYAN arrived in the world thirty minutes after his twin brother Roy and from his very first breath was obsessed about beating him at everything.

Their dad Luke was not present to witness the initial evidence of serial sibling rivalry. Roger nudged Roy over to get at the initial food supply. He bawled the longest and noisiest.

Luke Trevelyan was from a long line of West Country farmers, who, over three generations, had built up a thriving forty-five-acre concern at Compton Dando in the Chew Valley, half a dozen miles south east of Bristol.

He had not been around for the birth of his twin sons because on the night they arrived he was one of 82,400 engrossed spectators at the deciding Ashes Test match between England and Australia at West Ham Stadium.

For, apart from operating an illicit cider mill, motor cycling was Luke's greatest passion.

From his teenage years he had been an enthusiastic but none too successful competitor on the thriving West Country grass track scene. Like many men of the Mendips, he had been swept along by the speedway sensation, going with a gang of grass trackers to the first meeting at Cardiff on Boxing Day, 1928.

When Bristol opened ten years later he was a willing pits backroom boy for the new Bulldogs at Knowle Stadium.

He knew he did not possess the ability to make the league grade as a rider. But he was determined to give his fighting sons a head start.

He knew from bitter experience they had to be treated with scrupulous equality.

They had started brawling as toddlers over everything. Toys, balls, food, biscuits, beds, pillows, soap, anything would cause an argument. Although not identical, physically they measured up pound for pound and would fight each other literally until they dropped.

Desperate mum Maisie tried to keep them apart, gave them separate rooms, identical toys, birthday and Christmas presents.

With their identical armies of toy soldiers they fought the Battle of Waterloo and then each other because they both wanted to be the Duke of Wellington.

When they started school they both wanted the same desk and when they started to cycle, they scrapped over their bikes.

When they were seven years old, Luke thought it might calm them if they could channel all their energy and aggression into speedway. With the help of a few cronies from the West Country grass track scene, he built them identical 50 cc mini-racers and carved them their own 120-yard track with a farm tractor.

"You must be raving mad," wailed wife Maisie. "They'll kill each other on those bikes."

But something eerie happened.

Once the Terrible Twins had learned to slide their buzzbikes around the turns, they developed an intuitive understanding. They did not race each other. They raced together, side by side, shoulder to shoulder.

Uncannily, Roy always went inside Roger. It was telepathic.

Although fuel was rationed during the war, Luke managed to put by enough of his tractor ration to allow the twins to practice on their own during the later years of the conflict.

They were both naturals, but Luke could not be sure just how good they were because there were no boys of their age with facilities to race.

At the end of the war, when they were twelve, he moved them up on to 100 cc machines. They were fighting over schoolgirl sweethearts in gingham frocks, and football boots, and Bristol Rovers FC programmes, but seemed locked together on the track.

When Bristol speedway reopened in 1947, Luke took the twins to see their first meeting. They fought over who should sit next to him in his wagon. Luke fiddled them into the pits to meet two of the Bristol team, Roger Wise and Fred Tuck, both his prewar chums on the grass.

The twins were spellbound at the spectacle of the Bulldogs, in their orange and black body colours, sideways on around the tricky little 290-yard Knowle circuit. "That's all we want to do when we're old enough," they chorused. "We don't want to waste our lives ploughing fields."

"I'll get you a trial," promised Luke.

"Me first," said Roy.

"No, me," said Roger.

"You'll go together," said Luke. Incredibly, they did not argue.

By the time they were fourteen, the twins looked physically right to be motor cyclists: nuggety muscles, strong, shortish legs, developing shoulders and strong grips.

They had also developed West Country accents like clotted cream, and a taste for cloudy cider.

Bristol boss Reg Handcomb, another of Luke's prewar acquaintances, willingly arranged for the boys to have a trial on a borrowed, proper speedway machine.

Curiously, neither looked comfortable on his own on the track, although both clearly had a natural aptitude for shifting cinders.

"Put them out together and see the difference," said Luke.

Even the crustiest old retainers in the pits were impressed as they rode together, side by side. "They'll be a team riding sensation," said Handcomb. "No rider will squeeze past them, inside or out."

Speedway regulations did not permit riders to apply for an official racing licence until their sixteenth birthday. But the Bristol promotion revealed their local schoolboy discoveries to their public in an 'exhibition' during the interval of a Second Division fixture against Sheffield.

The choked terraces were intrigued as the two diminutive figures cruised up to the starting tapes.

Teenage speedway riders were virtually unknown. Most kids of school age couldn't afford a push bike, never mind a three hundred quid speedway unit. Second Division teams were predominantly staffed by riders with prewar experience, seasoned Australians, or ex-servicemen seeking Civvy Street excitement.

On average they were all in their thirties.

When the Trevelyans tore round together in dazzling duplication the Bristol crowd leapt to their feet. They could not be split as they crossed the line after four laps.

The ovation was spontaneous, the reaction varied.

The Bristol Evening World carried a double-page spread with pictures announcing:

Potential Speedway World Beaters Still At School in the Mendips. Britain's Youngest Cinder Princes Will Ride For Bristol.

The Speedway Control Board rapped the Bristol management firmly on the knuckles for promoting underage riders and outlawed any further public exhibitions by the boys.

"They should be restricted to cycle speedway," advised a stuffshirt in Pall Mall.

Barney Stacey, in the Speedway Gazette, whose antennae were inevitably tuned to a decent story, wrote an editorial:

England's speedway future could well rest with twin schoolboys from Cider Country who are not even shaving regularly yet.

The Trevelyan twins, schooled by their prewar rider dad Luke, will amazingly have over ten years speedway experience when they sign a contract for Bristol and are permitted to ride officially on their 16th birthdays in June.

By a crazy coincidence, they were christened Roy and Roger – and every filmgoer knows the hottest performer on screen right now is Roy Rogers and his horse Trigger. Like the twins he's a star of the West, too!

Knowledgeable sources down Bristol way insist the boys are at their best when riding together when they seem linked like Siamese Twins.

Bristol boss, canny Reg Handcomb says they will be the greatest team riding act in the sport once they find their feet in league racing.

They could be the most exciting thing to happen to British speedway in 1949. So watch for their arrival. Bristol are confident they are future world champions but are not sure if one is better than the other!

Reg Handcomb says you simply can't split them for talent and ability. Wouldn't it be just about the greatest story in speedway history if our sport had a run-off for the world title between twins?

Luke read the article and grunted. He knew that would also start the greatest ever punch-up likely to be seen at a World Final.

SPECTACULARLY headline-making weeks passed for Vincente V-Man Voltori before he was scheduled to renew his acquaintance with Jacko Rintzen at West Ham.

V-Man had been a considerable sensation in British speedway, not only for his on track success.

He had travelled to Birmingham and squared up to their Blond Bombshell following a racing incident and then caused a wonderful brawl in the Belle Vue pits after putting himself around fearlessly with the dour, no-nonsense Northerners.

Barney Stacey, who adored a colourful character, chortled in his weekly editorial:

This extrovert American has introduced a touch of the John Waynes to British speedway. He hits first and asks questions afterwards, both on the track and off. But boy, is he box office! New Cross is buzzing like never before. Folk are queuing round the blocks to see him everywhere.

V-Man's reception at West Ham was mixed. But it was mayhem. There were over 50,000 packed in for an ordinary league match.

Jacko was making final clutch adjustments with Chinners when V-Man approached him in the Hammers pits.

"How ya doing, cowhand?" he asked.

Jacko looked up.

"Good'y, Vincente," he replied. "Word is you've been causing a few stampedes."

"Just having fun."

"Well, have fun tonight."

"I sure will. Remember what I said. Watch your back."

"Not a problem. But you will see more of it than me. Because that's all you will see of me tonight. My back."

V-Man had never seen a circuit as huge and wide as West Ham. Belle Vue, another biggie, had made him think a bit and his tactics there had caused a riot. But he was well stoked to dish out some backstreet come-uppence to the apparently unruffled Aussie.

They met twice. As they cruised to the starting line, V-Man copied Jacko's 'no hands' routine adjusting his goggles. The New Cross fans roared with approval. It was their only consolation. All V-Man did see of Jacko was his back, disappearing away from him, almost the length of the straight ahead. The whole of West Ham chuckled with great glee.

A furiously frustrated V-Man collared mechanic Herb Call and said: "Hey, man. I just haven't got the horsepower to live with this guy. He's made me look a mug."

Call explained that V-Man's machine had been set up mechanically with the small New Cross track in mind. It was perfect there. He really needed another machine, with the timing and setting gauged for bigger circuits like West Ham. Maybe an extra high gear. But that might affect his starting.

"Well, we must do something for when I come here to ride again," insisted V-Man. "I'm not having that cowhand laughing at me."

"Come and spend time in the workshops next weekend," said Call. "We'll try and work something out together."

"Not this weekend, Herbsy," replied V-Man. "No can do. I'm going to visit an old Army buddy and raise a whole lotta hell."

CHAPTER 20

THE DOCKLAND postman humping around Custom House at sun-up every morning had no problems identifying the Perkins household in Freemasons Road.

Bedecked with red, blue, and white Hammers and a banner inscribed Cup Finalists 1949 it was clearly the address of speedway fanatics.

Since West Ham had won through to the final of the National Trophy and the chance of their first success in speedway's KO Cup, the Perkins family had existed in little short of a fever.

This could be a once-in-a-lifetime experience. They were determined not to miss a moment. But how were they to organise supporting their side? The first leg at home was no problem. Simply walk down Mortlake Road and across Prince Regent Lane, get in the turnstile queue earlier than they did every Tuesday.

But the vital second leg, away at Belle Vue (Manchester), that would need thought, organisation – and a minor miracle. Because the family could not raise ten bob between them to contribute towards the 500-mile round trip to Manchester.

Prewar, Alby and Rose Perkins had been regular fixtures in the West Ham Stadium crowd since speedway started there. You could hear the bikes, smell the burning fuel and oil from their squashed two-up, two-down terraced dwelling, which avoided being a slum thanks to Rose's diligent cleaning.

Alby had been jobless right through the Depression, forced to spend most of his time at home. With precious few pleasures, it was no surprise that Rose became pregnant in three successive years. Steve-oh, Leslo and Gina were dragged up on scraps until evacuated, with their names on a label attached to their collars, to Saffron Waldon before the Luftwaffe started systematically flattening their entire neighbourhood.

Luckier than some, they were billeted together and formed a close bond during their years away.

Their little home on Freemasons Road somehow survived with four walls still intact but the roof and windows shattered. Rose had spent seventy-six consecutive nights living like a potato in an underground shelter before moving in with her sister at Rainham, Essex, for the duration.

Alby had simply disappeared in one of the first nights of the firebombing. He had gone to muck in with rescue operations, never to return. Rose scanned the casualty lists without success. He had vanished. Many folk did at that time. But it left the family destitute, living on charity and goodwill of neighbours and relations. Alby was not officially dead so benefits claims were difficult.

The boys hastened from school at fourteen to seek casual work from the tallyman at the docks. Gina, tough and tomboyish, wanted to be a PT teacher so buried herself in to schoolwork.

Speedway racing was their only escape.

Rose did not attend after the war. She did not want to do very much at all, except listen to the radio. She sat gazing vacantly into middle distance. But the Perkins kids lived and breathed speedway.

Unable to find the shilling admission fee, the boys would bunk in over the stadium perimeter fence during the day of the meeting then hide in the cleaner's cupboard in the gents toilet, among the smelly mops and buckets.

Eventually discovered by ground staff, they were given free admission provided they stayed after meetings on a Tuesday to clear up all the waste paper and litter on the terraces.

They scavenged for old push bike parts and managed to build their own cycle speedway boneshakers, racing on bombsite circuits all over the East End. They were thrilled when one of their so-called skidkid colleagues, Ben Silva, graduated into the real thing and into the West Ham team. He was their special inspiration.

With a little regular money coming through from the casual dockland work, both the boys ensured that their kid sister had enough to go through the turnstiles too. She begged to go with them, but split inside the stadium to join nearly all her classmates, fighting to get a place around the pits.

She had photos of Jacko Rintzen and Ben Silva, cut from the Speedway Gazette, on the walls of the bedroom she had to share with her mum.

She had to be restrained from going to the Dorchester Hotel to attempt to inflict bodily damage on film starlet Jinxy Joynson when she heard she was to be escorted by Jacko.

The Hammers were in their blood.

And the team were in a Cup Final they simply could not miss.

SQUATTING alone in the scruffy pits area of a cycle speedway track around slagheaps abutting the Northern Outfall Sewer off Newham Way. Steve-oh and Leslo considered their options.

"No way we can raise the fares to Manchester on a train or the Supporters Club coaches," said Steve-oh. "We've got to get there under our own steam."

"Hitch hike?" said Leslo.

"Too risky," said Steve-oh. "No guarantee of lifts. We could be stuck by the side of the road on the bloody Snake Pass with our thumbs in the air for weeks.

"We can't walk. There isn't enough time. We've only got four days and one night between the first leg and the return at Belle Vue.

"There's only once chance. We'll go on our bikes."

"You're loopy," grinned Leslo. "They'd fall to pieces before we got to Watford."

"So we put 'em together again. We've built them up from nothing. What can go wrong we can't patch up? We can surely do fifty miles a day, maybe more. We can sleep by the side of the road. We've still got that old tent they used for emergency cover during the Blitz. We can scrounge food as we go and use public toilets to freshen up.

"If we make it obvious that we're speedway fans we're bound to run into other speedway folk en route who'll give us a hand and maybe something to eat.

"Reckon we cycle a couple of hundred miles a week practising speedway. It should be easy on the road. And we have all the time in the world to come home. Perhaps we can stop off to watch a meeting at Tamworth or Birmingham."

The Perkins boys had never seen speedway outside London.

But they were fired by the idea.

Both had sat listening, like Nelson's Childhood, at their Dad's knee when he regaled them with the legends of the Hammers' winning the National League in 1937 and Bluey Wilkinson's homecoming after winning the 1938 World Championship.

Now, another first.

A Cup Final.

They would one day tell their spellbound sons how they pedalled their push bikes to follow the Hammers to glory.

INEVITABLY, Gina insisted: "I'm coming too.

"And my friend Pat."

The Perkins brothers looked at each other hopelessly, helplessly.

"You haven't got a bike," said Steve-oh.

"No, but Pat has and I can borrow her sister's. You can't stop us. We'll go on our own if we have to. We were going to hitchhike there and back. Girls never have a problem getting picked up. But this way we won't have to fight off all the dirty old lorry drivers with their hands up our skirts.

"Mind" – Gina giggled wickedly – "My mate Pat quite enjoys all that."

Patricia Fenner was notorious both at school and around the streets and docks of E17 for her brazenness. She attached herself to most of the boys in her class like a vampire bat and left them drained of bodily fluids. She stunned the under-sixteen school soccer side by invading their dressing room and joining the team in the showers.

Her elder sister Viv was widely known across the East End as a Windmill Girl, a showgirl who posed, with only a strategically placed strip of sticking plaster, at the famous theatre in Great Windmill Street, off Piccadilly Circus.

Pat's ambition was to follow her sister, make a living being ogled. Physically, she was wonderfully endowed for the job. Morally, she had all the makings of an old-fashioned, golden-hearted Cockney raver. She was set to go far in Soho.

All the boys knew her fondly as Right Cow Pat.

"She'll be a good laugh with us on the road," promised Gina. "She always is. She never complains about anything except when she can't find a fella."

The Perkins brothers groaned and said: "But we'll have to doss down together."

"We all slept in the same bed for years when we were evacuated," retorted Gina. "Pat won't mind. She once slept with half the Plashet Panthers cycle speedway team in a caravan on Wanstead Flats."

Steve-oh and Leslo knew from lifelong experience their spiky-feisty kid sister, with her close cropped hair and chunky gymnast physique, would not be deterred.

She was a handful when roused.

She would be safer with them than let loose alone with Right Cow Pat.

They mapped out their route. Not too rigidly. Across North London to Watford. Up through Aylesbury to the A5 at Towcester. Bypass Birmingham and Rugby to the A51 at Lichfield. Then Newcastle Under Lyme, Stoke, Congleton, and into Manchester through Stockport.

"There will be days we can go further than others," said Steve-oh. "We might get a lift on the back of a lorry. We must be flexible, play it as we go. Get as many miles in early when we're fresh. Reckon it's vital we're in Stoke by Saturday morning."

They had time to write a letter to the Speedway Gazette. It read:

An Appeal To All Genuine Speedway Fans Between London and Manchester.

We are four skint West Ham Speedway fans determined to get to Belle Vue (Manchester) for the Second Leg of the National Trophy Final.

We plan to make the journey by push bike but would greatly appreciate any help along the way with overnight beds, any food or fruit that can be spared. We will carry our own drinking water.

We will be passing through Aylesbury, on the A5 and A51, Lichfield, Stoke and Congleton.

Any help that the great British family of speedway fans can offer will be very, very welcome.

Up the Hammers.

The reaction was encouraging.

The Belle Vue management promised that if the foursome got to the track in time they would be given free admission. The Belle Vue Supporters Club said they had members who could put them up for the night.

"They might not be so keen if Hammers beat 'em," mused Leslo.

They had offers of beds in quaint-sounding places like Steeple Clayton, Maids Moreton, Clifton upon Dunsmore and an old inn at Tittensor, where the guvnor was a Stoke Potters follower.

Several groups of speedway fans promised to watch out for them on the road with refreshments.

Down in the bowels of West Ham Stadium, the board called a meeting to discuss the situation. A proposal was made that the board should cover their travel costs with free passage on the Supporters Club coaches.

It was turned down flat by Vic Gordon.

"We'll get much, much greater publicity if they get there on their push bikes," he stressed. "We can boast we've got the most dedicated fans in the whole world.

"And folk who don't come to West Ham now will believe it must be something absolutely extraordinary if four fanatics are prepared to cycle 250 miles just to support the team. It could attract new customers.

"We can make a fuss of these kids if they manage to complete the journey. Let's promise them they can do a lap of honour with the team, hopefully parading the National Trophy."

He added: "My information is that one of the girls is going to work at the Windmill Theatre. So that's another good angle."

The Cup Final week approached.

The Perkins kids and Right Cow Pat were geared up to go. The boys had to fit lights and brakes on their cycle speedway machines. An East Ham cycle shop, which offered kindly aid to hundreds of skid kids, helped fit bulky double saddlebags. And supplied puncture kits, valve rubbers, and two jars of Vaseline.

"Cycling two hundred miles will put a new slant on the expression BSA," the shop owner observed. "Smear that on every day."

"Blimey, that sounds exciting," said Right Cow Pat.

The girls had much more modern bikes, with dropped handlebars and three-speed gear change. "Bet we get there before you," said Gina. "You're bound to be held up if somebody offers you a pint in a boozer on the way."

"Yeah, and you're certain to be delayed when Right Cow Pat cops off with some innocent geezer on the road," replied Steve-oh with spirit.

"Well, I won't be drinking or dallying," said Gina. "I want to see Hammers parading that bleeding Cup."

But all the chatter stopped when a wildly exciting new development caused furious speculation.

On the eve of the Final, West Ham completed transfer negotiations for a brilliant new Scottish prospect, who'd been given clearance by the Speedway Control Board to make his senior racing debut in the final.

CHAPTER 21

ALL VERY CONVENIENT, thought Iain Harman, as he deposited West Ham's cheque for £2,950 in the Glasgow Speedway Holding Account.

Purely by chance Ritchie had been required for publicity purposes by his demolition company at a convention when Glasgow had ridden their only National Trophy match of the season, away at Bristol where they were heavily beaten.

Speedway Control Board regulations would not allow a rider to appear for two clubs in the National Trophy in the same season. Ritchie was not Cup-tied, like every other half-decent performer in the Second Division.

Naturally Vic Gordon at West Ham had known that. It was convenient for him too. The deciding factor in his move.

What the London club did not know was that Ritchie's departure from Glasgow, although hysterically greeted with disbelief by the Tiger fans, was a heaven-sent getout for Harman.

Again there were irate parents and angry husbands making noises involving one Ritchie Mackay. He clearly hadn't only been scoring on the track.

Once again it was time to get out of town. London was a convenient world away.

Ritchie could not wait to sign the transfer forms. He would be on top National League money, almost double the Second Division rates. He would get a share on the National Trophy bonus fund if West Ham won the Cup. The Hammers were prepared to pay for a return ticket to Australia if he wanted to return Down Under during the winter.

He'd hit the big time double-quick.

Hearing whispers of his randy reputation, Vic Gordon fixed him with accommodation at one of his 'safe' addresses. There was a lusty nymphomanic widow called Madeline who kept a guest house in Parsloes Road, Barking. She thought she was Dorothy Lamour, always wore a flower in her hair, and sang Moonlight Becomes You every Saturday night at the Coach & Horses. Every rider that Vic had accommodated there seemed to have a permanent grin on his face. She was widely known as Barking Mad.

Everything dropped neatly into place for the first leg of the final.

'House Full' signs were out at Custom House thirty minutes before the scheduled first race. The stadium was pumping with raw excitement at the prospect of a Cup Final plus the debut of an interesting newcomer. The Perkins had queued since two o'clock to ensure admission. The girls elbowed their way almost on to the pits fence for an early glimpse of the new Scottish signing.

They were ready to leave for Manchester at sunrise the following morning. Their bikes were packed and prepared.

Forty thousand fans were willing the Hammers to build up a sufficient race points advantage to defend successfully in the return leg in Manchester.

That was the game plan. That was the script.

But Belle Vue had not read it.

RIVALRY between Aces and Hammers went way back. They had both opened for business on exactly the same day, July 28, 1928.

The Mancunians had been the powerhouse of speedway in the Thirties, winning the National League title four successive years before being eventually deposed by West Ham.

The Aces also had a fierce Cup-fighting tradition, winning the trophy five times in the Thirties and again in 1946 and 1947.

They had a rare poor season in 1948, failing to get in the honours and were desperate to start collecting silverware again.

Their captain was the vastly experienced England leader who had tried to talk Ritchie into appearing for the Lions in Australia.

He masterminded Mancunian track tactics for the first leg in London.

In a terse team talk, he said: "Don't be fooled by all the publicity. They are masters of bull here. Remember they have two team members out injured.

"OK, they've signed this Scottish whizkid but he's got no experience of racing at this level. He's greener than a frog's backside. Don't give him room to move. Intimidate him and the other kids in the West Ham side like young Silva.

"Concentrate on demoralising them. Let Rintzen go. Just pack in behind him. Hit them where they are vulnerable. If we can hold them to six points here we'll murder them in Manchester in the return.

"That Cup is our property. No mistakes. Tear into them. Concentrate on their inexperienced blokes. Don't let them settle."

Ritchie received a rapturous reception from the terraces but in his first ride in the legendary Crossed Hammers was facing the cagey England and Belle Vue captain.

And he fell for the oldest con trick in speedway.

As the four starters revved furiously on the grid, the Belle Vue man nudged the tapes. Believing them to be moving upwards Ritchie dropped his clutch and jumped the start. He was automatically excluded.

Welcome to the big time.

In his next ride, he was so anxious not to repeat the experience he completely missed the jump and could not make up a bike length on the tough, team-riding opposition. Hardly a dream start: two starts, no points.

Belle Vue were riding to instruction: dour, durable, giving nothing away, hitting the lesser experienced Hammers hard.

Jacko Rintzen was mixing it magnificently with the Northerners. But every time he attempted to shepherd his partner for a maximum heat win, Belle Vue would apply pressure. On three occasions he could only just consolidate a race win.

Ritchie discovered the starts and first turns in senior racing were a hundred per cent sharper and tougher than any he had experienced before. Elbows, shoulders, back wheels came flying at him.

"Don't try to mix it with this lot," Jacko advised him. "They're oldtime bike brawlers. Get out wide as the dirt moves to the outside. There's more room than you would think out on the fence."

Jacko was impressed that Ritchie had not been overawed by the competitiveness of the occasion. He could hardly have had a tougher baptism in top flight speedway.

West Ham rallied late in the meeting. Ritchie followed Jacko's wide-riding line, picked up a couple of second places in his last two rides.

West Ham won the first leg by four points. Belle Vue considered they had done their job and would waltz the return leg. It had been a classic Cup tie. But it was not over.

181

Gina and Right Cow Pat managed to get Ritchie to autograph their programme. "Bet he doesn't wear anything under his kilt," said Pat.

The Perkins party were all the more determined to get to Manchester for the return leg.

"The Hammers will need all the support they can get with only four points in hand to play with," said the boys.

The riders had widely varying ways of preparing for the Belle Vue showdown.

Ritchie went back into the warm welcoming arms of Barking Mad.

Jacko relaxed by heading for Surrey to feed the donkeys at Mule Terrain.

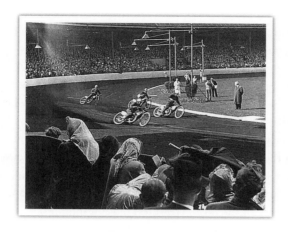

CHAPTER 22

FREQUENTLY freewheeling, acknowledging regular waves and toots from passing truckers, the Perkins Push Bike Crusade pedalled cheerfully out of north London. The weather seemed set fair, the roads were flattish, the girls in their skimpy shorts attracted attention.

Their West Ham banners catching the breeze, they found the old Watling Street route, Gina scowling as they passed Bushey Heath, near Elstree. "That's the film studios where that bitch Jinxy works," she sniffed.

The boys were aiming to make Aylesbury on their first day and were reasonably satisfied to make camp behind a friendly pub on a canal bank just east of the town.

They ate sparingly of the rations they had packed. The landlord of the pub provided stale sandwiches left over from lunch and unlimited water.

They pitched their tent successfully and settled down swiftly, aiming for a dawn departure. Right Cow Pat snuggled suggestively up to Leslo. "Got those valve rubbers handy?" she giggled.

But it was not a snug awakening.

September rain was streaming down in a depressing curtain as they freshened up in the pub toilets.

"Best to hit on as best we can," said Steve-oh.

By lunchtime they were drenched, miserable and holed up in a shabby transport café on the A413 below Buckingham.

The girls were offered a lift to Rugby by an unshaven truck driver. But Gina said:

"Nah thanks mate. We're a foursome. We're sticking together."

It was not a good day. It wasn't a comfortable night either.

As the wet weather persisted, the pedalling pace slackened. Although the girls did not complain, they were finding the going tough. They quickly appreciated the value of the Vaseline and forgot about skimpy shorts. They wore all the clothing and waterproofing they had.

By the Thursday evening, wet, weary and behind schedule, they were holed up for the night in the home of a friendly Tamworth speedway follower. He had seen their letter in the Speedway Gazette and offered accommodation.

The Perkins party could have a bath and reassess their position. Right Cow Pat offered to jump in with the boys. Weariness did not inhibit her.

"We're only just over halfway there," said Steve-oh. "We must have a really good long day tomorrow or we're not going to make it."

"We'll make it if the rain stops" said Gina. "But if Pat and me are slowing you down, you boys push on. We'll be all right on our own. We can meet up later."

"You're not staying on your own," said Leslo. "I'll stay with you. Steve is the strongest and one of us has got to make Manchester otherwise the whole thing is a worthless disaster."

The rain persisted so it was agreed Steve-oh would go on alone to try to make the seven o'clock start at Belle Vue. He would not stop for sleep. The other three kept the tent, stayed on the agreed route and if necessary would meet up again with Steve-oh as he was returning home.

He departed over the horizon north of Newcastle Under Lyme and, with the pressure off, the other three kept a more leisurely pace, even lazed for a couple of hours in a warm café near Stoke.

By Saturday lunchtime, the three stragglers were short of Kidsgrove, still doused in drizzle, with their West Ham flags drooping in the wet when two pickup vehicles with JAP speedway machines stowed in the rear went by, tooting merrily.

Then pulled up.

A very familiar thatch of strawy hair poked out of a window and said in an Australian accent: "Hey, you kids haven't got a ratsarse of a chance of getting to Manchester tonight. Reckon me and my mate can squeeze you in.

"If you've bloody cycled all this way it's the least we can do."

It was Jacko and Ritchie, travelling in convoy.

"My brother is up ahead somewhere," said Leslo.

"We'll pick him up if we pass him," said Jacko.

Gina simply sat speechless, next to her bedroom pin-up. Following with Ritchie,

Right Cow Pat inquired: "Do you ever wear a kilt?"

They reached Belle Vue with two hours to spare before the first race.

There was no sign of Steve-oh.

MAKING STEADY progress and confident of getting to Belle Vue in time, Steve-oh's rear tyre went bang near Bramhall, south of Stockport.

He had left all his kit with the other three so he had two options: leave the bike and run the rest of the way. Or ride with a flat tyre. Steve-oh concluded he would need the bike to get home again so the best option was to ride on with a squidgy tyre.

Crawling along, he was lost in a maze of identical Manchester suburbs when the first race started. He desperately asked the way from a bunch of scruffy kids playing hopscotch.

"Get to Piccadilly and ask for Hyde Road," they replied. Steve-oh clanked into the city centre, somehow found Hyde Road. He had recognised a landmark: the Big Dipper which he had read was right next to the first two turns at Belle Vue Speedway.

Bloody hell and damnation: he could hear the bikes! But in a panic he could not find a turnstile open. Frantically he dashed around the stadium perimeter, to the pit end, where he knew there would always be a gateman.

"Please let me in," he pleaded. "I've cycled all the way from London in the rain."

"Well, you've only just made it, lad," said the gateman. "There's only three races left."

IMMEDIATELY after the first leg of the National Trophy Final in Docklands, West Ham boss Vic Gordon summoned Jim Chinnock quietly up the two flights of cement steps to his office.

"I'm going to make mischief," he said. "And I need your help.

"We'll need psychology to help us defend our four-point lead.

"I want you to get hold of a fresh batch of methanol racing fuel. Say it's been specially prepared by a leading petrochemist so it has an extra kick – like the higher octane stuff our RAF pilots used in the Battle of Britain.

"I'll issue a press release first thing in the morning saying we're taking our own supply to Manchester for the second leg. I'll make sure the Northern papers get the story too.

"With any luck, Belle Vue will object and demand it's analysed. That will stir up the controversy. Belle Vue will believe we've an added advantage. It should give our blokes a boost."

Normal procedure regarding fuel supply in British speedway was that the staging track provided the dope, then deducted the charge when issuing the visiting riders' pay cheque.

It was unknown for teams to take their own fuel with them, although not illegal.

Gordon was gambling that this tactic would unsettle Belle Vue, inspire the Hammers.

The national newspapers splashed the story.

Hammers Secret Fuel For Cup Final Return, read headlines in big bold type.

Gordon smiled smugly when Belle Vue insisted they wanted a sample for analysis to ensure this hyped-up rocket fuel was legal.

Chinners obtained a drum of methanol from the usual distillery in West London, chalked 'Latest Batch – Secret' on the side, and made arrangements for its journey to Manchester in a huge white pick-up, with two stadium security men riding shotgun.

The West Ham team were instructed only to use Chinners' own special supply, and not the Belle Vue track issue.

It was all good old knockabout fun.

And, thought Gordon, it might just work.

Forty eight hours before the return match, Ritchie approached Jacko in the West Ham workshops, where most of the team were lovingly preparing their machinery.

"Can I ask a favour, Jacko," he asked. "Can I follow you to Manchester on Saturday? I'm still hopeless driving around and out of London and I'll be lost in Manchester. I can find my way to the Dorchester and meet you there."

"Not a problem," said Jacko. He had quickly grown to like this brashly optimistic young Scot. He might not have been so impressed had he known Ritchie had mischievious alternative motives.

The Scot, constantly hankering for the high life, was desperate to break into Jacko's starspangled social circle. He had admired the publicity about Jacko and his really fancy ladies like Jinxy Joynson and that upper crust cracker who had been Deb of the Year and was all over the society columns.

Imagine walking into a Glasgow hotel with a woman like that on your arm!

Ritchie reckoned if he moved alongside Jacko in his sort of circles he would surely rub shoulders with the right sorts and let his natural charm do the rest.

He did not know about Jacko's doomed affair with Fan.

Dashing, eligible, with a regular stash of ready cash, Jacko was in demand.

He had squired Jinxy around London on two further occasions. Her agent had

186

arranged it. Jinxy had said Jacko was one of the very few men she could trust. She wanted to see him again. Their conversations never really became intimate.

She introduced him into her studio set. Other stunning young actresses smiled appealingly in his direction. One only wore black. She kept spiders as pets and was called 'Tara' after one of her favourite tarantulas. She was in all the papers. She even wore black lipstick.

The Dorchester Hotel chambermaids were mystified when it appeared on his bed sheets.

Lady Charlotte invited Jacko to her father's country seat near Hurstpierpoint. Jacko would happily have slept in the superbly equipped stables. He rode a pure white hacker called Persil, one of the most handsome horses he had ever seen. The Sussex folk admired his equestrian skill.

In turn, Jacko was impressed by Charotte's horsemanship. He had never really ridden with a woman before. But she could manipulate a mount more intricately than any man he had seen. They rode frequently out on the downs. Jacko realised they were getting on well, getting close.

But he hauled in the reins when Lady Charlotte said: "You'll adore my stepmother. She's not much older than me and most awfully glam. All the chaps are absolutely dotty about her."

"Guess I'm okay staying with the horses," said Jacko. He had tortured memories about being left alone with awfully glam mothers.

Her Ladyship's country chums seemed totally insane. After swilling down champagne by the magnum after dinner, they agreed to go for a midnight gallop dressed only in their nightshirts.

Returning to his quarters, Jacko had discovered an auburn-haired stable girl called Larissa sprawled in his bed wearing only riding boots.

"I know you belong to her bloody ladyship," she said, in a frank county accent. "But I'm twice the woman she is and I always have all her boyfriends."

It was a wild life.

It was a wild life that Ritchie wanted to share.

INCREDIBLE, thought Ritchie, Jacko's fatal attraction for the sheilas can even conjure up tasty teenagers on a deserted stretch of the A50 in the rain.

Ritchie could hardly believe his luck. Right Cow Pat, although dripping wet and hair in rat tails, reminded him of a young Jane Russell. He had been bug-eyed with admiration when he'd seen The Outlaw movie and had nurtured nocturnal fantasies about the curvy brunette ever since.

The rest of the West Ham team were impressed when they rolled into Belle Vue.

"My life, Rintzen and Mackay have only brought a couple of schoolgirl ravers with them," said Ben Silva. "What a way to prepare for a Cup Final."

Vic Gordon was not nearly so entertained.

"Leave them with me and don't go near them again," he roared at the sheepishly grinning pair. "I'll fix them with seats and tell everyone it was all part of the publicity. You were being gentleman, doing a good deed.

"I'll take them home in the Oldsmobile. Chinners can pack their push bikes in with that funny fuel drum.

"We'll get the London newspapers to photograph them when we get home."

The Belle Vue management made a tannoy announcement seeking Steve-oh without success. They promised that if he showed up they would direct him to their seats in the stand.

There was no time to fret.

The National Trophy Final second leg had lift-off.

It also had downpour.

The weather had been wet for days and now Manchester was at its muckiest. The track was deep, rutted, a mudbath. The home side were accustomed to such conditions.

Very much at ease, too, was Ritchie Mackay.

He had learned his speedway on rough old slagheaps with the BAOR. They did not have track graders there. In Glasgow it rained as much as in Manchester. Ritchie was a confident wet track specialist. That was an unexpected bonus for the Hammers.

Because conditions did not suit Jacko.

He had learned his racing on dustbowls. His lightweight machinery jumped and bumped on the ruts.

Belle Vue were in customary mean mood. Traditionally, they were the most feared home side in world speedway. Jacko could recall being knocked about like a pingpong ball on the Manchester track before the war.

The Aces swiftly overturned Hammers' four-point advantage from the first leg. The Londoners were forced into a rearguard action, packing together to share the points in most races.

Belle Vue were not expecting the inexperienced Mackay, making his debut on the track, to be so effective. His points kept the Hammers in touch.

When bedraggled Steve-o Perkins arrived with three races left, the home side were two points ahead on aggregate and fielding their strongest pairings for the final push.

In heat sixteen, Jacko from the inside grid performed one of his most electric starts, threw his back wheel in a broadside at the first turn, spraying his rivals with flying cinders. Filling them in, as they said. But the tactics also blinded his team partner.

The Hammers held on to split heat seventeen, too, after an over enthusiastic home rider had turned turtle in a wild wheelie at the starting gate.

A last heat decider, for nominated riders, Aces only had to share the points. If a Belle Vue rider could win the race, the Manchester club would lift the trophy they believed was their personal property. West Ham needed a first and second to triumph.

Jacko was naturally programmed to ride, but Vic Gordon gambled on bringing Ritchie, who had started the meeting as a reserve, into the line-up. Belle Vue fielded two of their most aggressive, competitive home track specialist local boys

Jacko volunteered to take the grease-patch outside grid. "Just do what you've been doing all night," he said to Ritchie.

The huge crowd silenced dramatically as the four starters came under orders, engines screaming in the leaden air.

In grid two, Ritchie nudged the starting tape. The Belle Vue rider on his inside banged in the clutch, breaking the tapes, getting an automatic exclusion.

Ritchie was a quick learner in conmanship. It went right back to his days fiddling tips as a waiter.

Belle Vue down to one starter. Advantage West Ham.

As the three remaining riders prepared for the restart, with the Belle Vue crowd howling in indignation, Jacko said to Ritchie: "If this Belle Vue bludger makes the start, keep up, don't get tailed off. He'll be expecting me around the outside, so I'll try to fool him and move him over. Be ready to jump into the gap, I'll take him right out on to the fence."

The lone Belle Vue rider, a tough but talented Lancastrian called Lewis Luton, had the entire Belle Vue side, including their wily old captain, giving him advice and encouragement.

The Belle Vue crowd were making noises only previously heard at the Coliseum.

On the wet surface on the outside of the grid, Jacko's back wheel, spinning furiously, snaked him into the first turn.

Every Belle Vue fan leapt as Luton's blue helmet showed in front leaving the second turn.

Jacko needed two laps to close him down. Then he delivered his sucker punch, switching from the outside to the inside line leaving the pits corner. Shoulder to shoulder the pair hit the first corner of the last lap. Jacko did not turn, drifting, drifting, drifting, but ensuring he left his rival just enough room to race. But the soggy cinders were four inches deep out wide. The Belle Vue man was battling to stay in touch with his machine.

Jacko, too, was almost blinded by spray, but getting his wheels back in line, he glanced inside.

His first impression was a tartan scarf, blowing crazily in the wind. In front.

ON THE WILDEST occasion in the East End since VE Day, West Ham paraded the National Trophy the following Tuesday evening.

"Our greatest night since the England–Australia Test Match in 1933 when we had 82,400 in the stadium," said the company secretary, happily counting the bags of money bound for the nightsafe at the bank.

The Stratford Express had a five-column photo of the team on the front page, the trophy and the conveniently local Perkins kids holding the silverware aloft.

Right Cow Pat had a call from a lovely lady called Sheila Van Damm at the Windmill Theatre telling her to make contact when she left school. She had seen the publicity and read about Pat's ambition to follow in her sister's stiletto heels.

The Manchester Cyclists had been invited into the West Ham boardroom for the Cup Final success celebrations. Vic Gordon ensured press photographers attended. Gina followed Jacko like a puppy. He felt emotionally unsettled, haunted by memories of the last time he had attended the boardroom with a pretty East End girl, with a similar soft London accent.

Pat quietly obtained a contact address for Ritchie Mackay.

"I'll be sixteen in a couple of weeks," she told Gina. "And legally allowed to consent. To anything."

Jacko found himself lying to Gina and vowed he had never slept with Jinxy Joynson. "So there's still hope for me," she said, grinning cheekily, only half in fun.

Feeling incredibly old, Jacko smiled wearily and said: "Ah, Gina, lovely Gina. You will find a much better bloke than a cuss like me. Us outback types don't mix well with women. Reckon I'm destined to spend my days with dogs and horses."

"Won't stop me trying," said Gina, defiantly.

190

CHAPTER 23

ACCORDING TO the tourist books, France should waft aromatically of coffee, distinctive cigarette smoke and freshly baked bread, while echoing to intricate accordion music.

In Private First Class Vincente Voltori's experience it reeked of gasoline and rocked almost non-stop to slurping saxophones playing 'In The Mood'

Stepping off the train at the Gare du Nord, Paris, after a four year absence, he thought the place still stunk of cheap gas. When he had passed through Paris after VE Day, he had been just another freewheeling, good timing GI.

Now in his immaculate suit and tie, he could pass as a major corporation arms salesman as he hopped a cab and said: "NATO headquarters."

He had served nine months from D-Day, regulating the fuel pumping from England to the front, under the command of a quite brilliant service corps administrator. He'd been Major Courtney Clark Hartington then and he had adopted the V-Man as his sidekick and lucky omen after believing he'd saved his life.

V-Man had been panic dashing for cover from the last recorded strafing from an Me109 in Normandy, when he pushed the major into a ditch. Court thought he'd done it deliberately, unselfishly, and had kept V-Man under his comfortable command for the duration.

V-Man had read how his old commander's administrative skills had accelerated

191

him up the corridors of power at NATO HQ, where he was now a major general.

They had parted, almost legless on Calvados, singing "When Johnny Comes Marching Home".

What a surprise for good old Courtsy when I come rolling up out of nowhere, thought V-Man. We'll beat up Gay Paree together.

But he had to use all his charm and powers of persuasion even to get past the snowdrops (US Military Police), into the marbled, high ceilinged foyer of NATO. He had to leave his overnight bag with a grim-faced guard. A Master-Sergeant on the reception desk looked massively disinterested.

"Got a military pass" he snapped.

With his most disarming smile, V-Man said: "See here, pal. I'm just here to look up an old wartime buddy I haven't seen for years. Haven't you got any old chums you want to share a beer with? I'm sure if you get a message through to the Major General to say that Private First Class Voltori, the V-Man who saved his Goddam life, is in reception he'll get Eisenhower to give me military approval."

"Well, I'll try," said the Master Sergeant. "Wait on the seat."

Five minutes passed before a girl who could have stepped straight from a modelling session, with piled-high, immaculate hair and perfect teeth said to him: "Mr Voltori? I'm terribly sorry to have kept you waiting."

The lady simply had to be English. Boy, did she have class. She made the BOAC air hostesses look like burlesque chorus girls.

V-Man had become a little disillusioned about English girls during his first weeks in London. Sure, there were thousands hanging around the tracks. But they surely were not Vivien Leighs. V-Man could hardly interpret their accents. He was funny that way. He got kicks from ladies with sophisticated voices.

His team mates, grinning wickedly, had organised him a rumble with what they called a Track Spare. Her name was Stella Lane from Shooters Hill and she boasted the most magnificent breasts. In the New Cross dressing room she was fondly referred to as Mammary Lane. Her opening gambit to him was: "Great tits, ain't they? 'Ave you got a fag, mate" It was not the martini-sharp, cultured conversation that V-Man found so irresistible.

This apparition in the NATO foyer was much more the merchandise.

"That's oke," said V-Man. "I guess the General's kinda busy. But I got the whole weekend."

"I'm afraid he will be tied up for an hour or so with some unexpected problem which has just arisen in Trieste. But he seemed quite pleased to learn you were here in the foyer. He asked me to take you to the Staff Canteen for a coffee. I don't suppose you'd prefer tea?

"I'm Major General Hartington's Personal Assistant.

"I'm Ann Harris. Hello."

FOLLOWING the slender, slightly swaying figure in the tight-fitting, calf-length, charcoal-grey skirt, V-Man thought: "Take as long as you like, Courtsy boy."

With two very decent cups of coffee on a table between them, V-Man said: "You've just got to be English. That accent slays me. How come you're in old Paree?"

"Oh, is the accent so pronounced? I was hoping I was losing it in Paris after nearly a year. I love working here. Paris can be fun. I've almost forgotten England.

"But what about you? What's your connection with the General?

You don't look remotely like any of his normal acquaintances"

V-Man felt his hormones twitch. All the broads he'd known would never have used a term like "normal acquaintances" That was exactly the kind of thing which turned him on.

"We served together in Normandy. He looked after me like I was his kid brother. He was under the impression I saved his life."

"Oh, what happened?"

"The only Kraut plane we ever saw was shooting us up. I was trying to save my own neck and pushed Courtsy to one side, into a ditch. He was sure I'd done something, what's the word they use, valorous. We were buddies right through to the end. But I lost contact when I went home and he became the main man, top brass.

"Only just managed to get back to Europe. He's the only pal I've got here. So first off, I gotta look him up. Wanted to see Paris, too."

"I'm sure the General will show you around. May I ask what your business is in the States?"

"Catering"

"Is that what brings you to Paris?"

"No. I'm here in Europe on other business. Guess you won't have heard of a ruckus called speedway racing?"

Fan felt her intestines do a spectacular back flip. Her breath caught. Surely, surely, this couldn't be true. Coincidence simply didn't happen this way.

V-Man noticed her reaction.

"Hey, whadda I say? You know speedway? That's impossible."

"Yes, I know a little about it," she said, trying to recover composure. "My family used to live quite close to a London track. You could hardly help but notice it. But what's your actual connection with speedway?"

Fan considered V-Man's beautifully cut suit, a proper white shirt and tasteful tie. Fan had a fad about men in proper shirts and ties. She did not care for men in demob suits, collars two sizes too big, and awful ties with palm trees painted gaudily on them. This attractive American could easily have been a stadium owner, or restaurant franchiser. He didn't dress like a rider. He can't possibly be a rider.

"I'm a rider," said V-Man.

Again, Fan felt dizzy.

"Oh, really. Can I ask where you ride?"

"New Cross, lady. I'm the toast of the Old Kent Road."

Fan had to drink deeply at her coffee to get a grip of her emotions.

New bloody Cross. It did not seem yesterday she had made a fool of herself, sitting alone in the New Cross Stadium restaurant, screaming like a schoolgirl over Jacko Rintzen. Afterwards they had laid together in the darkness and dared to talk about a future together. This couldn't be happening to her.

V-Man was sharp enough to realise that the lady was just a little flustered.

"Hey, have you got some hang up about speedway? I didn't mean to upset you. I just race for fun, for a laugh. What's with it with you?"

"Oh, it's absolutely stupid of me. It's just that, well, I used to know somebody in speedway and you reminded me. It's nothing really."

"You're kidding me. Who did you know in speedway?"

"Well, it was nothing really. But his name was Jacko Rintzen."

V-Man did a deft, rebalancing adjustment to stop falling from his chair. He clapped his forehead, dislodging his fedora.

"Lady, you have GOT to be kidding. You knew the cowhand? Well, I have sure heard EVERYTHING now. The goddam cowhand. I can't escape from that guy."

"I thought you might have heard of him. Why do you call him cowhand? He's been in speedway for years. I thought he was quite good. Do you know him?"

"We've met."

Fan bit her lower lip. This was absolute nonsense and she should drop the subject right now but she heard herself saying: "How is he getting on these days?"

Still shaking his head, V-Man said: "Cowhand? Jeez, he's the big cheese, head honcho. Goddam superstar. Red hot for the world championship later on.

"Living in fancy hotels. In all the papers with ritzy movie star dames and squiring society ladies."

Ridiculously, Fan felt her lips tightening, a nasty little pang pinging around her abdomen. "Oh, really. That doesn't sound a bit like Jacko"

"Sure thing, ma'am. Just can't imagine a classy lady like you would know a stumblebum like Cowhand."

"Oh, it was nothing really. We just lived near West Ham. I think he was more than a stumblebum"

There was an intercom call for Fan. The Major-General was sorry, it was unavoidable, he simply could not get away to reunite with Mr Voltori until tomorrow, when he would love to meet for lunch at The Officers Club on the Penthouse Floor. He would leave the necessary accreditation with the Master Sergeant. Would she please make the arrangements?

When she passed on the details, V-Man said: "OK, that's swell. Because now you've got to come to dinner with a lonely stranger in town.

"Strictly no turndowns. We got plenty in common, lots to yak over. I'll pick you up at eight. Please. Write down the address. Please."

No, no, no, thought Fan. Stop this right now. Say I'm sorry and walk away. Tell him you're engaged, you've got a date, tell him anything.

But don't be tempted. Don't be the world's biggest fool again.

She wavered and was lost. For some absolutely unaccountable reason she discovered she wanted to hear again about London speedway. She didn't want to leave it suspended in midair. She had to go on. It was like a drug.

"I'll meet you at your hotel," she heard herself saying. "You will never find my apartment out behind the Left Bank. Where are you staying?"

"Yahoo, lady," whooped V-Man. "Paris really is magic. I'm at the Hotel de Paris."

"I'll be in the cocktail bar at eight," said Fan, coolly, hardly believing her own voice.

"That's just great. I've got time to make arrangements. Oh, and tell Courtsy not to be late for lunch."

MIRROR, MIRROR on the wall, who is the craziest of them all. Fan smiled wanly at her reflection and again told herself: "This simply can't be happening to me."

After nearly a year in Paris, she was confident she had finally shaken off the shackles of Jacko Rintzen, erased the memories.

And yet. And yet...

Night after night she had lain awake in her apartment, listening to the sounds of Paris, feeling just a little lonely, a little sorry for herself, and wondering stupidly if she had been absolutely fair to blank out Jacko so totally. She could not forget her last words to Diana: "I don't care if you drive over a cliff." Maybe she was blaming Jacko for her own guilt. Now that the agony of her mother's death had eased, she had to admit to herself she knew who had made all the running in their liaison.

She'd seen her Mum devouring men. And deep down, she knew that Jacko would never, ever have forced his attentions on any woman. She'd virtually had to drag him into bed herself.

But now the bastard seems to have changed, she told herself, surprisingly angrily. Film stars in fancy hotels, indeed. He seemed to have forgotten her quickly enough. The bastard. Once again her mind raced over the same stupid logic. But surely Jacko could have stopped her Mum's seduction? Surely he could have pushed her away? He'd said he'd done it enough with all those doxies who throw themselves at speedway riders. The bastard.

Then, maddeningly, another dangerous thought would unsettle Fan. Should a meaningless snatched moment of physical contact be permitted to change her life forever? Goodness, time was quite a healer.

Fan had lived more like a nun than her mum during her time in Paris. Her mother had left her a surprisingly hefty legacy, she could afford an apartment, albeit bijou, in a stylish, fashionable district of the French capital. The property in Green Street had a complicated leasehold and was still in the hands of solicitors and property dealers. She was reluctant to return to try to sort it out. It would remind her too painfully of her kick in the knickers. She had created a new life in Paris. She had carefully bought new clothes. She fondly imagined she was acquiring Parisian chic. Well, just a little.

She had grown quite close to her boss, the upwardly mobile Major General, and, she had to admit to herself, would have required very little persuasion to have slid between the bedsheets in his impressive NATO courtesy apartment.

But Court was an oldstyle, Colonial American gentleman. Very proper. Though they had discreetly dined, held hands and he had hinted he would take her back to Kentucky to meet his folks, he had been distinctly cool about anything faintly physical. Fan had quietly learned from other officers in Logistics that he was sort of pledged to the daughter of longstanding family friends "from the county". There was an "understanding."

Subtly applying the final touches to her make-up, Fan smiled to herself and thought: "Talk about cupboard love. Why does my lovelife have to be so secret, so damned discreet? It isn't my nature at all."

Why else would champagne seem to be fizzing in her intestines at the thought of an evening with an outrageously brash but dashing American cavalier she had hardly met, who had rattled chains from her romantic past and actually knew the only real love of her life.

It could only happen in Paris, she thought.

And, dammit, I want to hear more about Jacko. Ridiculously, she thought she could smell speedway again, feel the frisson of the terraces at West Ham.

V-Man had a bottle of the lightest French Chablis waiting in the bar at the Hotel de Paris. "Have a drink, courtesy of New Cross Speedway, fair lady. Then we shall dine at La Vie En Rose. And you can tell me the story of your life. I just love to hear you English talk," he said, with a courtly gesture.

There was certainly nothing secretive nor discreet about a date with Vincente. He entered the Left Bank restaurant like a movie star, had booked a prime table out on the boulevard, hailed the maitre'd and sommelier like long lost relatives. He was the absolute opposite of boyishly shy Jacko and fearsomely formal Court.

Despite herself, Fan realised she was having fun. Whoa, girl, go steady on the wine.

She wanted to know more about America. She had heard of Hoboken, his early home. Didn't Frank Sinatra grow up there?

"Three blocks uptown," said V-Man. "Didn't stray much into our territory."

He told her about San Diego, sandblasting in the Mojave, and Las Vegas, which sounded unreal. Fan realised she wasn't far short of enchanted. It sounded a different America than the one described by the Major General.

They were into a heady bottle of red wine – "La Crema Christa, the Tears of Christ," said V-Man – when he casually enquired: "So what was your deal with that cowhand Rintzen?"

Fan felt another little electric shiver and replied: "Oh, we were quite good friends for a while. West Ham Speedway is part of the way of life in the area where I used to live. And he was their biggest star.

"My mother and I were guests of the West Ham board a few times and we met him in the boardroom after racing."

"And didn't he ever come on to you?"

"You mean ask me out?"

"Yeah, he must have been nuts if he didn't?"

"Oh, no. It was nothing like that," Fan buried her head in her wine to avoid his eyes.

V-Man hailed a cab for Fan and did not attempt to ride back to her apartment with her. He kissed her gently on the cheek and said: "I intend to walk back to my hotel and wallow in what remains of a romantic evening in Paris. It was a real great night. See ya tomorrow."

"Tomorrow?"

"Yeah, I'm meeting up with Courtsy lunchtime and we're gonna make Paris burn. But surely I'll see you sometime?"

"Oh, yes, yes. I'll make sure I come down to reception."

Fan lolled back on the taxi seat and realised she was rather dizzy. Or maybe it was the wine. Good God girl, she thought, after all you've been through you can still react like a ridiculous schoolgirl to a crappy line in chat up. Or maybe you're just bloody randy?

But she would ensure she didn't miss Vincente on the morrow. A girl had to live a bit dangerously sometime...

THE OLD COMRADES Reunion hardly set Paris ablaze.

Court greeted V-Man warmly. There was much backslapping but he only had time for luncheon in the NATO canteen.

"Shit man, I was reckoning on raising hell with all those Folies at The Crazy Horse Saloon and having ourselves a real time," said V-Man.

"Sorry, Vincente, no can do," replied Court. "There's a really tricky diplomatic issue with Trieste and the Yugoslavs and we've got a supply logistic headache. I simply do not have the time. Besides, Major-Generals can't afford to be seen around with can-can dancers. The damned Russians would make great political play of any scandal."

"Jeez, what a boring old bastard you've become, Courtsy," replied V-Man. "Well, if you're not available I'm going to lure your delicious Personal Assistant out again."

The Major General frowned slightly. "Ann?" he said. "Good God, have you seen her already? She did not say anything. She's far too good for you, soldier, not your type at all.

"But she is fascinated by America. She wants to see Kentucky but I can't imagine what mother would say if I took an English secretary home with me."

V-Man just shrugged. But he thought: then don't lead her on, you pompous, jumped-up sonofabitch. I know what Mama would say if I took her home.

That I'd hit the goddam jackpot in the lottery of life.

No, Fan wasn't doing anything that evening. No, she'd never cruised the River Seine on the Bateaux Parisien. Yes, she'd love to and would be at the bar of the Hotel de Paris, same time. She didn't want to let Vincente near her apartment. She didn't trust herself...

It was one of those make-believe evenings. Paris had surely never looked better, with the subtle illuminations on Le Louvre and Notre Dame. Vincente had later squired her to a backstreet Italian restaurant, established before the war and Mussolini had strained Franco-Italian relations with his territorial ambitions on the Riveira.

V-Man had been hailed like a prodigal, instructed the chef on making zabaglione and joined the waiters in a hilarious chorus from Verdi's Il Trovatore. Fan realised she hadn't laughed so much in a long, long time. She found herself wondering what this crazy character would look like against the backdrop of her London streets. How would he measure up against Jacko? Gosh, that was dangerous thinking.

"Gotta go back to London tomorrow, Ann," said V-Man as they parted, still very politely. "But it's been a real ball. And I still haven't heard the story of your life. But I'll be back."

"My life story isn't worth knowing. But you know where to find me."

CHAPTER 24

ONE WEEK before the twins' sixteenth birthdays, a sharply dressed stranger in a brand new Jaguar eased into the Trevelyan's barnyard at Compton Dando, wanting to see Luke.

"I represent Harringay Speedway," he announced. "The Racers management want to put your twins on contract."

Luke brushed his stubble and replied: "Oh ah. But they're committed to Bristol. That's where they want to ride. And that's where I want 'em to ride."

The Harringay agent, still business-like, added: "The club are prepared to provide them with machines. And we will reimburse you for the expense you've gone to in training them. The club are taking a considerable gamble."

"Well, they'm don't have to," replied Luke. "My lads already own good JAPs, I don't expect anything for getting them going in speedway. It stopped 'em fighting all the time.

"But you can talk to the lads and see what they say."

Roy and Roger were goggle-eyed admiring the Jaguar when they were summoned to meet the Harringay man. God, they look like choirboys, he thought.

"This 'ere gentleman wants you to go to London to ride at Harringay," Luke told his sons.

"But we're going to Bristol," they replied.

"There's a party of over a dozen girls from our old school going up to Knowle when we ride there next week.

"Ain't no way they can make the trip to London to see us."

So the Harringay last-minute poaching deal died stillborn, although Luke half promised he would contact the North London track if and when the boys were good enough for senior racing.

But Luke knew from his contacts that Bristol had ambitions to become a senior league side. And that perhaps the twins would help project them into the bigtime.

SEASONED customers on the terraces at Knowle Stadium thought there seemed to be extra hundreds of pigtailed girls in gymslips thronging around the pits on the night the Trevelyan twins made their official racing debut.

They were programmed in the second half of a Second Division match against Fleetwood. The Lancastrian visitors were not the greatest box office attraction.

The twins were.

Nearly a dozen photographers jostled on the infield, flashbulbs popping, when they lined up at the start, the youngest riders in post-war speedway.

A much more experienced 'junior', who was nearly twice their age, made the start from the outside. But Roy and Roger, shoulders almost locked together, tucked in behind and rode side by side for four laps and over the chequered flag.

Speedway racing did not boast such technicalities as photo-finish equipment so the judge/timekeeper, perched in an eyrie on top of the main stand next to the ACU steward, said: "Can't really separate them. Call it a deadheat for second place."

Thus the boys were carved into speedway posterity: twins deadheating in their debut rides.

Rick Eldon wrote in the Speedway Echo:

Hans Christian Andersen couldn't have made up a story like the debut of the Trevelyan Twins.
It will be a question posed in sporting quizzes for the next 50 years.

They continued to be sensationally newsworthy. The following week, Roy accidentally nudged Roger on the first turn, hanging him out to dry on the safety fence, and went on to win.

Before he had time to return to the pits, Roger had wrestled him to the ground on the infield before they were separated by Luke, who had done it many times, and track staff, speechless with laughter. Back in the pits, Roger threatened his brother with a spanner.

There was another gallery of pressmen when they made their team debut, as reserves for the Bulldogs. Wilf Eden set up a photo shoot with a pair of bulldog pups.

Luke, near exploding with parental pride, had to drive them everywhere. They were too young to hold a road licence.

They went to London for the first time, to appear at the new, glamorous Walthamstow track off the North Circular Road but insisted Luke took them down the Underground so they could ride an escalator.

They went to Scotland for the first time and gazed in wonderment at the hills of the Lowlands. Mountains, they decided. Much bigger than the Mendips.

Everywhere they appeared they attracted hundreds of schoolgirl followers in ankle socks. They signed school exercise books; one shiny-eyed nymphet requested their autographs on a copy of Enid Blyton's Sunny Stories.

Everywhere they appeared their uncanny togetherness won acclaim. "They seem joined at the hip," reported the Speedway Gazette Scottish stringer Jock Watt. "They're the best team riding duo in the Second Division."

By September, they were established in the reserve berths of the Bristol team and had given new impetus to the Bulldogs' season.

Luke had one more standout experience for them in this landmark year in their lives.

They would go to Wembley Stadium for the first time to watch the 1949 World Final.

CHAPTER 25

WEMBLEY'S World Final crept up on Jacko like a cat.

At every turn there seemed to be a reminder.

From his regal repose in Park Lane, Jacko relished strolling around one of the most traditional and stylish areas in England's capital: across to Hyde Park Corner, down Rotten Row, past The Serpentine, Birdcage Walk, on up The Mall to Buckingham Palace.

He rubbernecked like a tourist at the Changing of The Guard, marvelling at the precision of the soldiery. It stirred an instant memory of the 1938 World Final, the Massed Bands display on the manicured centre green.

A similar reminder as he attended Horseguards Parade for the Trooping the Colour. What a spectacle.

Jacko even had a jolt when, casually amused, he idled listening to the outrageous ravers at Speakers Corner. Among the Flat Earth and Drink Urine advocates, one tinpot despot was blaring on about world domination.

World domination. At speedway that meant Wembley.

I'm beginning to get a touch twitchy about it, admitted Jacko to himself.

Every rider had to qualify on merit for the Final. The lower division riders, like the cheerful guys Jacko had met at Poole the year before, had to work their way through the early rounds. Their top scorers progressed in the Second Division rounds. Ritchie had missed out there, while the Trevelyan twins had not been old enough to enter. The ten highest scorers from that section moved into the First Division rounds. That's where Jacko came in.

The leading sixteen scorers went to Wembley. Nobody was seeded. No bonus points were carried forward. The new world champion would be the highest scorer from five starts on the night at Empire Stadium.

Jacko safely negotiated his rounds. One was at his home track, West Ham, and, as the Stratford Express insisted:

Nobody is better than Rintzen at Custom House. If they staged the World Final in East, instead of North London, Jacko would be a cert for the title.

Rintzen J. was in the top three qualifiers. Now he simply had to ensure he avoided the shocking pre-big night luck that had torpedoed his chances in the two preceeding seasons. The *Stratford Express* had a front page screamer: No Mistakes This Time, Jacko! They dished out over 20,000 Whacko, Jacko rosettes to the fans.

When on that September day Jacko and Chinners edged up Wembey Way through the milling multitudes towards the Pits Entrance, way down to the left of the Twin Towers, Jacko knew that this time he'd beaten his bogey.

He was ready for the greatest night of his speedway life.

EERIE SILENCE engulfed the North dressing room at Wembley Stadium.

Jacko had passed through the eighteen-feet wooden gates that guarded the eighty-yard sloping tunnel that led to the pit area on the third and fourth turns.

There were famously two dressing rooms – for home and away teams in soccer. Only the North room, on the right hand side as you entered, was used for speedway.

It had a lofty ceiling, concrete floors, benching, a huge tiled bath, curiously with outside piping, which formed a framework six feet above the water.

Intrepid naked speedway riders regularly climbed monkey-fashion up the piping to divebomb the water with impressive splashes.

No such frivolity on speedway racing's most important occasion in over a decade. None of the usual pre-meeting banter about madcap antics involving extrovert speedway characters from Edinburgh to Exeter.

Jacko thought he could not be better prepared.

Together with Vic Gordon, Chinners and other experienced West Ham mechanics, he had decided on a World Final plan.

Chinners knew a Northern-based master-tuner called Eric Bincock, who specialised in preparing razor-sharp clutches. He had been used to 'breathe' on Jacko's.

Chinners had obtained his own supply of methanol racing fuel and kept it at what he was sure was exactly the right temperature. There would be no possibility of getting a flat batch from the track supply.

It had been firmly agreed Jacko would use a new rear tyre for each of his five starts. There would not be time to change tyres between races, so the West Ham workshops produced five separate rear wheels, each fitted with new tyres.

It was agreed to stick to the battle plan whatever unfolded on the night.

The World Final programme was twenty heats, with sixteen finalists meeting each other once. Starting gate positions, which could be critical, were allocated as equally as the format permitted.

The draw system meant that three riders would have two successive heats. Jacko was the first, in heats four and five, then had regularly spaced outings in heats twelve, fourteen and nineteen.

He would have the outside gate in heat four, then the inside in the following race. Jacko and Chinners decided that was to his advantage.

In a World Final there were no easy rides, but some were less difficult than others.

Jacko was grimly aware of his main rivals: the crafty, veteran England captain from Belle Vue – Jacko would be in his favoured outside start position against him in his opening ride, hopefully before he had time to settle; the technically-superb American Wilbur Lamoreaux – Jacko had used his throwaway tyres in his down-and-out days at Wimbledon before the war; The Blond Bombshell from Birmingham, dashing but not that effective at Wembley; and three of the Wembley Lions, one of them Stan Prince, always a huge threat as home track specialists. But any one of the finalists could emerge on the night as a surprise package.

Jacko fastened on his Australian national flag body colour, turned right out of the dressing room door and walked towards the cone of daylight and the pits area at the end of the tunnel.

You heard Wembley before you saw it. You smelled the pits, the burning methanol, long before you reached them.

Britain was still gripped by austerity, the pound had been devalued 30 per cent, even the hands on Big Ben had lost four minutes. Over 500,000 fans applied to the Wembley box office for tickets and the 100,000 who were allocated admittance were determined to make their World Final a greater, more emotional event than the Olympics or the FA Cup Final.

In the pits, Chinners, miraculously in a clean white overall, was tinkering with Jacko's clutch, all around a solid wall of sound, a kaleidoscope of colour. The Massed Bands marching meticulously, the knitwork of spotlights picking out the brass instruments on the counterpoint.

As Jacko strolled out on the tarpaulin-covered greyhound track to watch the bands – he had grown to love British pageantry – the entire North Bank behind him erupted in ecstasy. West Ham had taken over the entire Pits Corner as usual. Jacko waved shyly, his heart skipping. These must be the greatest speedway fans on earth, the most loyal folk.

When the parade was heralded by fanfares and 'The Entry of the Gladiators', Jacko felt his neck hairs stiffen just as they had when he watched his first Final back in 1938.

This was ultimate sporting theatre. And at last he was centre stage.

As each rider was introduced on the start line, Jacko peered up into the ocean of heads packing the home straight between the Twin Towers, trying to pick out Bongo and his wife, sitting among the West Ham complimentary allocation.

They had flown in specially for the big night. Bongo had packed on the pounds, looked ridiculously prosperous and viewed London with a gaping jaw.

Another electric thrill tiptoed up Jacko's spine at the thought his oldest friend and original speedway mentor, way back at Baranga Showground, was here to share this technicoloured experience. He earnestly wished that Kerslake could have been present, too. But he had indicated he was far too old to leave the cattle station.

When the finalists returned to the pits to begin the serious business, again the entire North Bank went hysterical with Hammermania. Even the home riders from Wembley looked impressed.

Chinners brought him down to earth. "Watch their line, watch their bloody line in the opening races. And learn."

WITH HIS GROWING reputation and recognition, reticent Stan Prince was emboldened to strike out.

After years of assisting disinterested, often boozy stringers with their grammar and syntax while taking their copy, Stan, like his Dad before him, nurtured quiet ambitions to write himself.

He asked Barney Stacey if he could submit a couple of columns to the Speedway Gazette.

They had been well received. To his astonishment, Stan was paid as much for one article as he could earn in an eight-hour shift taking copy. The *Speedway Gazette*, like the sport it recorded, was at its peak. With a mix of flowery editorials, name writers, fan pictures, pin-ups, films and show biz, it was circulating up alongside *Picture Post* and *Filmgoer*.

As the 1949 season reverberated into renewed action, Stan was able to quit his Fleet Street shifts.

He was riding and writing. Making news in more ways than one.

Stan grew in confidence and performance as the season unfolded. He was no longer in awe of the senior men in the Lions side. His new Pride of the Lions tag was proving apt.

By the time the World Championship qualifying rounds were staged, Stan had scored regularly enough to be among the thirty-two riders seeded direct into the final rounds. He had been drawn at Wembley and New Cross, two tracks suited to his style.

He scraped into the World Final, the third, and most unfancied, of the Wembley Lions to make the big night.

He was asked for his reactions (in a thousand words) by the Gazette. Stan wrote:

> *Don't read this – it's impossible.*
> *A boring copy typist nobody from a London backstreet next week appearing before 100,000 fanatics on the greatest stage, the biggest night, in the post-war miracle that is speedway racing.*
> *Five years ago it was an impossible daydream in a grim PoW camp in Poland.*
> *But Stan Prince will be there.*
> *Like I said, don't read this, it's impossible.*

Further into the magazine in his preview of the Final and assessment of the sixteen competitors, Barney Stacey wrote of Stan:

> *Least experienced of the Wembley riders. Unfashionable but could emerge from the pack. Listen for the Lions Roar if their local boy does deliver a shock.*

Just another day at the office, thought Stan.

He could have his tea with the family, roll up into his usual parking space, dressing room peg, and pits space, way up on the righthand side where the home team were housed every Thursday. Familiar faces everywhere.

While most of the other finalists twitched and fretted over tyres, track conditions and matters mechanical, Stan found himself more concerned that Dorry had brought her mum.

She would want to sit in the Royal Box.

AS HE CRUISED to the starting line for the start of his first ride adjusting his face scarf with both hands, in a mounting crescendo of noise, Jacko suddenly felt eerily alone. Accustomed to the loneliness and solitude of the Australian outback, he thought he was on a planet of his own.

As the green under-starter-orders light came on and the riders strained until the referee, way up between the Twin Towers, released the starting tapes, Jacko fixed his entire concentration on the magnetic solenoid at the bottom of the starting gate. When that flicked down, a nano-second before the tapes were released upwards, Jacko dropped the clutch and powered the revs.

It was not the greatest start he had ever made but with the clear outside run shortest journey to the corner, he had half a length of elbow room. Jacko chopped the corner, flicked out his back wheel, and blocked his three outside rivals, including the dangerous England captain, trapping them on the inside line. In pitside parlance it was known as throwing a back wheel.

He had three clear lengths into the back straight, all the track and sweet fresh air up front. As he chose his own line, flat-out past the pits he was briefly aware of a blurred mass of blue and red of West Ham.

Chinners engine did not miss a beat. Jacko was twenty-five lengths clear at the chequered flag.

He had no time to acknowledge his reception, speeding back to the pits to change back wheels for a new tyre, before being called up for his second race. Chinners was still fussing with chain and clutch as Jacko cruised into the inside gate.

This time he could watch the inside post solenoid on his left hand and made a perfectly coordinated getaway. He glanced across to his left at the thirty-yard line, knew he had at least a length in hand, and smiled tight-lipped under his face protector. Again a thrown back wheel spreadeagled his rivals and he emerged clear of the field.

He was briefly attacked down the inside entering the pits turn but out in the drive around the fence he was never going to be overhauled.

Two races, two wins.

Jacko now had a nervy seven-race wait until his third outing, when he would be facing the wily American Lamoreaux and the whirlwind Blond Bombshell. And he would be in gate three, which was tricky, a worry.

He sat on the squat wall which surrounded the greyhound track, distantly watching the racing. There were repeated hold-ups and pile-up incidents. Every finalist recognised his chance for glory. Nobody was giving an inch. The English riders particularly were fired up at their home HQ, before a partisan home crowd. Although rightly regarded as the world's leading speedway nation, England had still to produce a world champion.

Jacko was aware that the Wembley contingent, with their home track knowledge, were quietly avoiding the carnage and becoming a threat.

Jacko was the only unbeaten rider when they went to the tapes for the start of the vital heat twelve.

In grid three, he was unable to utilise his solenoid starting technique and was sandwiched between Lamoreaux and the Blond Bombshell, who was revving, and toeing the track, and holding up the start on his outside.

When the tapes went, Jacko was aware of even greater backwheel drive and the rider on his outside rearing and bucking in a wild wheelie, costing him yards in the run to the first turn. Presenting Jacko with the perfect opportunity for his favoured outside line around the first two turns.

Although on the inside the American had made a clever, effective start, he was vulnerable to Jacko's blazing outside overtaking down the back straight and seemed shaken to be chopped mercilessly on the pit turn.

Jacko was still increasing his lead as the chequered flag fell and a 100,000 people leapt to their feet to salute a rider who seemed unstoppable.

Although it was over midway through the meeting when track conditions traditionally got rougher, Jacko had recorded the fastest time. Now he had beaten all his most dangerous rivals.

Back in the pits, Jacko tore off his helmet and shouted at Chinners: "Dunno what you did to the bike that time, but it was better than ever, perfect. I don't reckon we should change anything. Just leave it as it is."

Chinners was adamant. "We all agreed beforehand that you would use a new tyre in every race. We agreed we wouldn't change that race plan whatever. You can't afford to miss your next start. You're outside Stan Prince, and he's clever, he's been lucky, he's been picking up points and he's in with a chance of winning the title.

"We change the wheel, OK. Agreed?"

Jacko nodded. Chinners was never wrong. And he knew how he would handle

Stan the Dribbler. He wouldn't leave the inside line. There would be acres of room for Jacko around his favoured outside territory.

Jacko had ample time to consider his racing tactics. The interval, after twelve races, seem to drag interminably. Jacko's deep seated appreciation of the Guards marching band began to wane. He was relieved when they strode smartly past him down the tunnel.

He felt curiously, icily calm as he prepared for the most momentous race of his life.

The usual routine: both hands off the handlebars as he adjusted Ruthie's face scarf as he cruised to the starting tapes. He never gave Stan Prince a glance. The frenzied arena hushed so dramatically Jacko felt he could have heard a tear drop.

He was in a world completely on this own as the green light at the 30 yard line flashed on signalling all four riders were under the ACU steward's starting orders.

The Dribbler rode immaculately fairly up the first turn and immediately glued himself to the inside white line.

Jacko attacked the apex of the corner, swinging his body weight instinctively, turning the machine in a perfectly executed broadside, ideally placed to blast away down the outside, grippy line of the back straight.

One hundred thousand riveted fans gasped, seemed to suck all the air from the evening, as his back wheel developed a mind of its own, skewed hopelessly, and highsided Jacko into the cinders piling up against the safety fence.

A puncture.

One of those five new tyres, so lovingly fitted and carefully checked, must have had an infinitesimal fault.

The craziest, the simplest of defects, which could happen to a vicar riding a push bike down a country lane, had cost Jacko Rintzen his chance of winning the World Speedway Championship.

Typically Jacko had landed softly. He was unhurt.

He had a long walk back across Wembley's magnificently manicured centre green to the pits. A track staff worker pushed his bike, the back tyre squashing and splodging drunkenly. Chinners materialised on the green, put an arm around his shoulder as they walked together.

The huge crowd fell silent They knew no rider had ever run a last or failed to score in a race and won the world title. But as Jacko slowly passed the Royal Box, the entire stadium rose to applaud.

Jacko looked up and saw thousands of hands clapping, whirring together like a million butterflies. As he walked, head down, across the track back to the pits, the entire North Bank was waiting for him.

In harmony, a cascade of sound…

They fly so high
 Nearly reach the sky
Then like my dreams they fade and die.
Fortune's always hiding.
I've looked everywhere.
I'm forever blowing bubbles.
Pretty bubbles in the air.

West Ham was singing for Jacko at Wembley.

CHAPTER 26

FROM his very first moments of awareness in a stifling back bedroom at Baranga, Jacko had never been a sniveller.

His ingrained stoicism surfaced as he returned to the Wembley pits and emerged from an avalanche of sympathisers.

He grinned ruefully at Chinners and said: "Guess we'll have to change the wheel for my last ride. Stick on that one I used before. She was a beaut.

"Oh yeah, another thing, Chinners. Shoot out to the wagon and fetch that spare West Ham body colour in the boot."

Jacko was determined to make a gesture for his wonderful, emotional West Ham followers.

He removed his Australian race jacket, pulling on the Crossed Hammers.

Vic Gordon arrived, grinning broadly when he saw what Jacko was doing. "You'll get a slap on the wrist from the authorities for removing your official body colour," he said. "But you'll be bloody immortal down the East End. You can still finish third overall. There's two-fifty prize money – and the West Ham board will double it."

"No worries," replied Jacko. "I'm going to enjoy myself now."

When he emerged from the pits, every West Ham fan immediately identified their team colours. To a man, they stood. No singing. Just clapping. It was the sort of respectful ovation afforded to Winston Churchill by the US Congress.

He was on the outside again in heat nineteen, relaxed but fiercely determined to finish in extra-special style.

As the starting tapes rose, his throttle-clutch synchronicity was as perfect as he had ever achieved. The super back tyre that had extra magical gripping quality bit evenly into the starting surface.

Jacko literally jumped out of the start. He seemed to be at the thirty-yard line before any of his rivals had moved a bike length. He was ten lengths clear by the apex of the first turn.

Rick Eldon, in the Speedway Echo, declared:

If men competitively ride motor cycles for the next 100 years, they will never achieve a greater, faster start than Jacko Rintzen did after shocking luck had again robbed him of world championship glory.

From my vantage view, right above him in the Press Box at Wembley Stadium, I will swear he actually flew for the first 30 yards of heat 19.

So Jacko finished third overall in the World Champtionship, unbeaten by man, robbed by ill fortune. Stan the Dribbler, with his carefully controlled style and calculated risk-taking, had emerged from the frantic pack to win a place among speedway's immortals as England's first world speedway champion.

Jacko rode at the back of the Wembley tractor on the victory parade with a still slightly surprised Dribbler at the front milking the applause and wondering how his wife would spend the five-hundred-pound winner's cheque.

A very gentle lady, the wife of the British Prime Minister, presented the awards and said sympathetically to Jacko: "You must feel like crying."

Jacko just shrugged. Only dogs and horses made him cry.

Barney Stacey, whose words were written in stone in immediate post-war speedway, reported eloquently:

As the lights were dimmed and the delayed rain beat upon the Wembley Boulevard of Broken Dreams, 100,000 speedway fans struggled homewards. Drama can be as exhausting to the spectator as it is to the main characters in the piece and the 1949 World Championship was high drama.

Local boy Stan Prince rode his home track, within himself and his luck to write himself into speedway and sporting folklore forever as Britain's first world champion.

Yes, Prince was crowned king — but the ace of hearts Jacko Rintzen was once again trumped and cruelly robbed of glory.

Long after the atom bomb has driven the peoples of the earth to underground habitation will old men stir in chimney corners and renew the trail of arguments left by the first post war World Championship.

But if they are still arguing into the 21st century they will surely agree that Rintzen's Big Night bad luck is beyond explanation. Beaten by a rotten puncture — pass the sickbag, nurse.

Or that there will never be a more emotional Wembley moment than West Ham's multitudes serenading Rintzen with their sentimental anthem. Not a dry eye in the East End when for years to come they recall Rintzen hauling their colours up the mast for his last race.

Truly, fortune's always hiding for this unassuming Aussie who has given speedway such media impact this summer.

Let us hope his dreams, though faded, will not die.

For he has given British speedway three glorious summers.

AT THE WORLD Final interval, after ten races, the BBC radio commentator live on the Light Programme was all excited about the style and dash of leading scorer Jacko Rintzen but added: "There's a lucky bluebird flying around Wembley tonight. It seems to fancy the shoulder of local boy Stan Prince."

Stan had run an unremarkable second first time out, with one rival excluded for jumping the start and breaking the tapes.

He had been tailed off at the rear in his second outing when the three leading riders, all pumped up with adrenalin, had tangled in a mad mixture of men and machines.

In the three-man rerun, neither men nor machines seemed to have recovered fully, enabling Stan to pick his well-worn line around Empire Stadium for three more points.

Third time out, he benefited from another shockingly ragged start, emerging down the back straight in front. Stan knew the shortest racing line around Wembley and was a difficult bloke to overhaul.

At the interval, a hum rippled down the terraces as they realised unfancied Stan Prince was in with a shout, second overall.

But he had unbeaten Rintzen outside him in his next ride.

Stan was aware of the tumult as he made his way sedately to the start line for the critical heat fourteen. He did not even glance across at Rintzen. He concentrated entirely on his line around the first corner. He knew Jacko would hit him wide and hoped the other two riders in the race would get in his way and give him a chance to get clear. Then Jacko would have to put his neck on the line around the fence.

Stan would stick to his tactics. He was not the type of rider to mix it with shoulders and elbows going sideways at fifty miles an hour. He knew he would come off worse.

He made a decent start, in reasonable shape at the first corner, when he became aware of a flying shadow on his right shoulder. Exactly as feared, Rintzen was going to gobble him up.

Then, something odd.

Rintzen simply wasn't there any more.

Stan saw the red stoppage light flash, eased off, sensing the awful drama of the moment. Clearly Rintzen had fallen. Rotten break. He was excluded from the rerun, cause of the stoppage. The bluebird had settled on Stan's shoulders.

Almost in silence, Stan won the rerun. Then the Wembley fans woke up. Lions flags everywhere, except the deflated West Ham end of the arena. The local boy was set to win. He would be England's first World Speedway Champion.

It was almost beyond belief. Like the entire story of post-war speedway racing.

In his final outing, one of the reserve riders had to be called in to replace a finalist who had been knocked about in the earlier bunfighting.

Stan also faced his Wembley captain, now out of the running, next to him on the starting grid.

"Just you start, Drib," he said. "Get out in front and I'll cover you. Win it for Wembley."

Neat and tidy, Stan made the start, picked his groove, and wheel-perfect made no mistake. With his back covered by his track-crafty captain, it was a simple sixty seconds until the chequered flag signalled the end of perhaps the most dramatic night in twenty-one years of speedway racing and four years of post-war sport in Britain.

The traditional tractor ride, the presentation ceremony, had a dreamlike quality. Jacko grinned rueful congratulations. He was the darling of the crowd, received the greatest ovation.

Stan found himself posing on the podium for a battalion of photographers, holding aloft the huge championship trophy, sponsored by the Sunday Dispatch.

"Funny," he thought. "I once applied for a job at the Sunday Dispatch."

Somehow, Dorry had found her way down from the stands, broken through the security men, and rushed towards him, arms outstretched.

218

In a firework display of flashbulbs, she grabbed the winner's cheque and screamed: "Ooh, Stan. Now we can buy a house on Hampstead Heath!"

WOMEN, grimaced Ritchie Mackay.

They surely make life difficult for a fellow.

He was naturally included in the West Ham party travelling to Wembley to watch the 1949 World Final, the first global summit for eleven years.

He was still gobsmacked by the roar of London. He did not want to miss this extra special night. He was rooting for his pal Jacko. The fella deserved a break. He'd been a real pal when Richie was like a little boy lost in senior speedway.

Ritchie could sense the history of the occasion.

Then sex raised its troublesome head.

Like virtually every inhabitant east of Tower Bridge, his lascivious landlady, Barking Mad, wanted to be at Wembley. She expected Ritchie's guest ticket as a matter of certainty.

But he could imagine the reaction if she swept into Empire Stadium wearing a lotus blossom behind one ear and looking like Dorothy Lamour in Road to Morocco.

Secretly, he had also been seeing Right Cow Pat Fenner, who stirred his loins and imagination like no female he had previously known. But he knew Vic Gordon would go ballistic if he knew of their liaison.

Pat was going to Wembley, no question. But she wanted to go with him. She wanted the world to know about her relationship with Ritchie. It would help her intended stage career to have such a glamorous boyfriend as a cinders star.

It was all getting out of control. His lovelife was always thus.

Almost immediately after the World Final, Ritchie had a passage booked on the Empress of Australia for Perth and another winter racing Down Under. Like a sailor with a woman in every port, the ship could not up anchor quickly enough for him to escape.

He still had not solved the problem when he received a surprise call. Mrs Bess Coleman, his long time fantasy lady from the Glasgow White City office.

"I'm going to be in London for the day finalising my divorce," she said. "Do you still want to treat me to that meal in a fancy hotel?"

It was the same day as the World Final.

A right bastard, but it provided Ritchie with a very attractive get-out. There would be other World Finals. Women like Mrs Coleman might come along once in a lifetime.

He gave his tickets to team-mate Ben Silva, told his miffed mesdames that he could not attend Wembley as he had to go to Southampton to supervise the freighting of his equipment to Australia. There was no alternative. Sorry and all that. He dearly wanted to take Mrs Coleman to the Dorchester but he was known there through Jacko. Awkward questions could be asked.

But the Ritz, famous for its cuisine and style, was just around the corner from Park Lane, fringing Green Park on Piccadilly.

He booked dinner for two and, optimistically, a room overlooking the park.

Mrs Coleman turned every head as she walked into the lounge, with its marble pillars and restoration murals. She was wearing the very latest, hour-glass New Look from Christian Dior, giving the impression that she had stepped straight out of The Tatler.

The very fancy lady I've always promised myself, thought Ritchie, smugly. Cracked it.

Mrs Coleman flashed her lashes and said: "This is much, much better than the Railway Hotel, Glasgow. You have come up in the world, young man."

Ordering a large gin and tonic, she added: "I completed my divorce less than an hour ago. I'm a free woman, and quite well-off, too. How would you like to be the first conquest of my new life?"

Ritchie did not put up a fight.

So while drama of theatrical proportions was stacking up at Wembley and his pal Jacko Rintzen's luck hit an unprecedented low, Ritchie Mackay was in bed in the heart of London's West End with the most uninhibited divorcee of the day.

When the pair eventually stopped for breath, Ritchie switched on his bedside radio to hear the sports news on the Home Service.

His language blistered the bedhead when he learned of Jacko's demise.

"How awful for your friend," said Mrs Coleman. "I suppose you wish you had been at Wembley now."

Ritchie grinned like a cat with a cartload of the choicest cream.

"Och no, I'd sooner be here than anywhere in the world," he said. "My time at Wembley will come."

WAY UP BETWEEN the Twin Towers, frequently having to stand to see over the heads of the packed rows of seated fans below them, the Trevelyan Twins drank deeply of their first Wembley experience.

They had seats in the same row as the Bristol team members. All around them were rider spectators from other tracks who, barely three months earlier, had simply been names in speedway magazines to them.

Wembley overwhelmed them.

"'Tis like wonderland," whispered Roy.

They were fascinated to read in the programme that brothers had once finished first and third: the Americans Jack and Cordy Milne in 1937.

There were brothers in with a shout in 1949: the greatly respected – and fancied – England skipper from Belle Vue and his younger sibling from Wimbledon.

The twins paid rapt attention to the form of the only Second Division rider on parade, Ken Le Breton, the colourful 'White Ghost' in his pale-painted leathers. They had actually raced against him at Glasgow Ashfield. He'd beaten them. But not out of sight.

The twins were awed by the style of Jacko Rintzen, devastated by the fortune that robbed him of the title.

"Look and learn from Stan Prince," said their dad Luke. "He's clever. You don't have to go roaring about like a mad ha'porth to win titles."

They stood quietly, watching the 100,000 crowd ebb away into the dampening night.

"We'll be back here, dad," said Roy.

"Ah, our turn will come," said Roger.

My God, how in Heaven's name will we separate them? Luke thought.

VINCENTE V-Man Voltori did not feel inclined to attend the 1949 World Championship Final at Wembley as a spectator. He had arrived far too late in the season to be able to compete.

He had other, more attractive distractions.

In Paris.

And not with his old Army buddy.

CHAPTER 27

AS MELLOW autum mists drifted down the River Seine, Fan Harris felt her pulse quicken and heart skip a beat as she packed the more modest of her Parisian fashion acquisitions and accessories.

She was returning to London.

She told herself it was imperative she cleared up and signed the necessary documents for the sale of the Green Street property.

But she knew, she had to admit, there were other, deadly emotional reasons behind her return.

She had contacted her old friend Jessica in Theobalds Road to arrange a lunch reunion. Jessica had revealed Jacko had been trying to find her. Trying to find her! Jessica added she had told him she thought Fan was going to America with some US Army officer. GI bride and all that.

Fan's mind had been in turbo-charged race mode.

If Jacko had been whooping it up with all these ritzy pin-ups why on earth would he creep around to her former office to try to make contact? After all this time. Why, why, why?

Vincente had made it a memorable summer. Somehow she had managed to keep their relationship out of the boudoir. He had been unexpectedly patient. But Fan knew she was weakening. He would be returning to the States in a matter of weeks, and, being the character he was, might never return.

She had some mighty decisions to make.

Vincente was meeting her off the Fleche d'Or at Victoria and had offered to book her into a West End Hotel. That would have been tempting fate too dramatically. And her resolve. She had made arrangements to stay with family at Upminster, insisting it was convenient for her East End business with the property.

With an inward groan, she also realised it was convenient for West Ham.

It was a genuine pleasure to see Vincente. He was immaculately turned out, as always. It seemed he always made a special effort when he met her. She simpered at the thought. She really did fancy him. But could not get Jacko out of her mind.

Somehow he had acquired a Buick and drove them to the Hyde Park Hotel for a drink. She would guide him on to Upminster later.

In the cocktail bar he grinned wickedly and said: "You'll never guess where you can see me struttin' my stuff on a sickle. Gotta booking for the last big meeting of the season at West Ham."

BY LONGSTANDING tradition, West Ham's gala final meeting of each season was The Cesarewitch. It coincided with the greyhound racing classic of the same name which was staged at the stadium the same week.

Vic Gordon billed it as bigger than the World Final.

There would be an all-star individual line-up bidding for the £250 first prize. Because he was well aware of V-Man's box office reputation – and his widely chronicled edgy rivalry with Jacko – he had booked him for the meeting.

He also knew V-Man's appearance would attract about 5000 New Cross fans through the Rotherhithe Tunnel to attend the meeting.

Several days before the meeting, V-Man quietly collared Herb Call in the New Cross workshops.

"Gotta do something about West Ham, Herbsy," he said. "My motor just wasn't fast enough last time round there. And I got very special reasons for wanting to hit it big in this Cesarewitch, whatever that means."

The wily New Cross mechanic replied: "We've got time to build you another motor into one of the New Cross spares. Your own simply isn't set up for a track the size of West Ham."

V-Man closed conspiratorially in on the mechanic: "Sounds good, Herbsy. But

I've heard word that some guys get the drop by using a bigger motor than the regulation 500c.c. Can't you work your magic and conjure up a bigger motor to provide a bit of extra power?"

Experienced workshop operators knew an oversized engine can be created by enlarging its cubic capacity, relatively easily achieved with a technical alteration to the flywheel, preferably an unused blank. "Got a blank flywheel then" was a sarcastic pits comment directed at riders suspected of running an extra powerful motor. Herb Call sniffed sardonically: "You've been mixing in shady company, Yank. If you get caught using a big 'un you'll be banned and run out of town. The other blokes might just lynch you, too."

"What the hell?" grinned V-Man. "It's my last meeting over here. I'm heading back to the States at the weekend anyway. Give me extra horses, maestro."

"Well, I wouldn't if it was a team meeting," replied Call. "And it's right against my principles."

"Just do it, Herbsy. I'll accept all the blame if we're caught. Goddam it, bore me a big 'un. I'm not having that sonofabitch cowhand sticking his ass up my nose this time around."

NEW CROSS had made arrangements for Fan to be a guest in the West Ham Restaurant and afterwards at the reception in the Boardroom.

Only Vic Gordon recognised the name Miss Ann Harris. Guest of Vincente Voltori. Gawd, thought Gordon, this is going to be comical. All the riders always attended the last meeting reception.

Grimly Gordon considered: "I may have to apply my former skills as a bouncer at Ilford Palais if it gets a touch heated."

Fan was surprised by the warmth of her greeting in the restaurant from so many of the guests. The Track Doctor hugged her and said: "I was so sorry to hear about your mother. I shouldn't really say this but I have to be honest, Ann. Her driving always worried me.

"It was only natural you should want to get right away from it all. But I always knew you and Jacko would get back together. You were made for each other, girl."

Wincing slightly, Fan said nothing.

She felt pterodactyl-sized butterflies fluttering internally when she saw Jacko for the first time on parade. He did not appear to have changed one bit. His reception from the crowd was tumultuous. Never mind the world, he was truly the 'People's

Champion' By contrast, Vincente was greeted like a pantomime villain. He still stood out in his V-painted leathers.

Jacko still looked like a matador.

Vincente looked like a gladiator.

Fan felt a cold sweat. Maybe this wasn't a good idea after all.

DOWN IN THE PITS, the New Cross workshop staff were warming up two machines for the V-Man. His own, and the Herb Call-doctored special, which was making a noise like a tank battle. Other blokes in the pits were looking quizzically across at the irregular racket in the New Cross corner.

Before the first race, V-Man sauntered across to Jacko and said: "Hiya, cowhand."

"Good'y, Vincente."

"Brought an old friend of yours along as a guest tonight."

"Friend of mine?"

"Yeah. Her name's Ann Harris. Met her in Paris. She works for my old Army CO. She said you were acquainted."

Jacko said nothing for a few heartbeats. "Fan? She's here tonight? With you?"

"Whaddya call her – Fan? Jeez, she's more than a fan. She's a real lady. Guess she will come over to say hello after the meeting."

"That would be nice."

V-Man had no idea of the impact he had made. Jacko waited until he had returned to his pitspace, then quietly moved to the pits fence to scan across the vast sea of heads to his left, up to the restaurant in the vain hope that he might be able to identify Fan. Dozens of girls around the pits screamed his name.

Crazy but somehow he could feel her presence. "Fan, Fan, you're back," he thought. "It doesn't matter a ratsarse about Voltori. If you're back there must still be a chance for me."

Ritchie Mackay could see something was troubling Jacko. "Has that bloody Yank been winding you up," he asked. "Don't let him worry you, Jacko. You'll piss all over him."

"Aw, it was nothing. Just brought up a name from the past."

Unsettled Jacko was not really concentrating on racing but that hardly mattered. Everyone was stunned by the performance of Vincente Voltori. He was flying by everyone. The New Cross crowd contingent were euphoric. Their man had wings. The illegal cubic capacity of his motor was a terrific advantage on the pacy West

Ham circuit.

When they met, Jacko outgated him, but had been reeled in down the back straight like a game fish. More hysteria from the New Cross crowd.

After the race, Jim Chinnock grabbed Jacko and cried: "Nobody goes by your motor down the straight like that. That bloody Yank must be on a big one."

"He's certainly going darn quick," said Jacko, quietly "Maybe he's just got everything set up perfectly for conditions tonight. Remember that set-up at Wembley that worked so well for me?"

"He went past you down the bloody straight," insisted Chinners.

"That simply isn't on. We should ask for the engine to be measured."

"Aw, I'm deffo not going to rat on him," said Jacko, never a sniveller.

"You might not," retorted Chinners. "But other folk will."

British speedway had set regulations regarding complaints about oversized motors. It had to be made officially to the ACU-appointed Machine Examiner at the track and a cash deposit put down to cover costs. The offending machine would then be impounded and measured in appointed and approved workshop facilities. If it was found to be over the 500c.c. limit, the offender faced an automatic suspension.

Chinners and two other mechanics persuaded Vic Gordon to slap down the deposit for an official measurement.

By the time the official party approached the V-Man pitspace he had switched from his workshop special to his own machine. It was mission accomplished as far as he was concerned. He had whipped the cowhand on his own heap. With Ann up there in the stand watching.

When the Machine Examiner said he was impounding his engine V-Man retorted: "Jeez, you guys are shitty losers."

"Which is your machine?" asked the Machine Examiner.

"This one," said V-Man, pointing to his own. "Surely everyone knows my handlebars."

"Bollocks," shouted Chinners. "You've been using that other one. It's making more racket than the Flying Scotsman."

"Exhaust problem," said V-Man, grinning hugely. "I've been using this one. Feel the head. It's still hot."

A group of riders, including Jacko, had gathered around, looking uneasy. Ritchie Mackay observed: "There was a fella riding a big 'un at Claremont when I was there. Somebody shoved a handful of sugar in his fuel tank." Herb Call had slunk away somewhere to hide.

"Right, I'm impounding this machine," said the Examiner, starting to wheel away

V-Man's wide handlebar unit.

"Stone the bloody ravens, surely you riders aren't going to let him get away with this," yelled Chinners. "You tell him which bike he's been using. He's cheating on you. He's getting away with the three card trick."

Not one rider was prepared to protest. Nobody would rat on a colleague. It was the curious code of the cinderfellas.

"I shall have to withdraw from the meeting," said V-Man, dramatically. "Can't use my spare. Exhaust problems.

"I shall watch the rest of the meeting in the restaurant with a special lady friend."

FOR ONCE, Jacko did not wallow in the bath after the meeting, soaking up the scuttlebutt.

He changed quickly and, with Ritchie Mackay, who was also on his own, headed from the dressing room down the corridor under the stand to the Boardroom reception.

Even bold Ritchie had not dared to take Pat into the Boardroom only weeks after she had left school. She had been at the meeting, though, after spending another day of her 'apprenticeship' at The Windmill Theatre, learning the difficult art of depilating her pudendum.

Fan was sitting at a table with V-Man. It was typical of him that, having caused such a furore in the pits with his machinery, he had boldly fronted up at the Boardrom reception. Most riders would have run for cover, not daring to show a face. It did not seem an issue to V-Man. He hadn't won the meeting. He settled a score with Rintzen. So what the hell? Speedway was only a laugh anyway.

Jacko strode across, his face splitting in a spontaneous grin.

"It's a real pleasure to see you again," he said to Fan.

Fan's breath seemed to catch. Those were almost exactly among the first words Jacko had spoken to her in what seemed years ago at The Bugle, Hamble.

"Hello, Jacko," she said. "It's nice seeing you again too. And congratulations."

Although unsettled all night, Jacko had finished third in The Cesarewitch, pocketing a £75 bonus. It was more than Fan earned in three months.

Ritchie hovered up, carrying drinks. Bloody roll on, he thought, Rintzen knows another dazzling female. "Oh, you haven't met Ritchie," said Jacko to Fan. "He's our latest superstar."

"Hello, Ritchie," said Fan. "I love your tartan scarf."

"Gosh, where did Jacko find a woman like you?" grinned Ritchie. "And what are you doing with this crazy American?" He turned to V-Man and retorted: "Hear you're switching to 750c.c. US Flat Track Racing in future?"

Sensing distinct friction in the air, Fan said quickly: "Oh, Jacko is an old friend. And Vincente is a new one. I seem to be fatally attracted to speedway riders."

"We should be so lucky," said Ritchie.

Jacko recalled the last time he had seen Fan, burning with hatred, at her mother's funeral. Now she seemed the old Fan again. The world seemed a beautiful, brighter place to him.

As the party grew noisier, the V-Man moved away to talk to the Catering Manager of West Ham Stadium. Other riders were cold shouldering him. Jacko made sure he found himself alone with Fan.

"My friend Jessica said you had gone to my old office looking for me," she said.

"Just worried that you were okay."

"Didn't she suggest you contact me in Paris?"

"No, she sort of said you were all tied up with some high flying American officer and were all set to go to Kentucky or somewhere.

"I was pleased for you and thought the last thing you would want was contact from me. Wouldn't have been the go. Right time to back off."

"Courtney and I are only friends. I don't know where Jessica obtained her information."

"Got another American friend now. It must be pretty wild with Vincente."

"Yes, it surely is. But I've heard that you have some pretty wild friends now, too."

The V-Man burst into their conversation. "Hey, you guys seem to know each other better than I thought. Listen, we're all going on to party at Bertorellis. Why don't you join us, cowhand. I'm heading home next week. It's a farewell beano."

"Yes, why don't you come," said Fan. She was fascinated by the total contrast in these two characters who had so taken over her life.

"Aw, thanks, but I guess not," said Jacko. "Not so keen on Italian food."

"Then don't eat, just drink," said V-Man. "Old times sake, man. No hard feelings."

"Reckon not. But thanks for the thought."

"I expect Jacko has other glamorous friends to go on to in Park Lane," said Fan, suddenly chilly.

"Well, I've got other friends. But they're not in Park Lane."

 "Oh, Elstree Studios, maybe?"

"Gawd, no. I'm staying at a Donkey Sanctuary right now and I've got a few dear old jackass friends who will be waiting for their carrots."

The Track Doctor whisked Fan away to talk to a couple of florid men who appeared to be corporate directors of the greyhound company.

She welcomed the escape. Well, didn't you put your Parisian stilettoed foot in your impeccably made-up little mouth then, she thought.

That bloody Jacko Rintzen was priceless. He could have every woman in the West End but he's more concerned about the comfort of a bunch of old pit ponies.

Idiotically, she felt goosebumps popping and banging. She was getting that oldtime feeling. Crazily, she was warming to him again.

She was really, really glad she had returned.

She looked across the Boardroom where Jacko and V-Man were in animated conversation. Well, Jacko was listening and V-Man was talking and making sweeping gestures. It was odd but all the other riders did not want to speak to V-Man. She didn't know Jacko wasn't talking about speedway. He was discovering just how deep her relationship with Voltori went. He appeared relaxed, reassured.

How did I get involved with these characters, she thought. And why oh why do I find them both so damned exciting.

She knew instinctively that she was going to be drawn back to them, and to speedway, like a dozy moth to a phosphorus flame.

God help me, she sighed.

How AM I going to end up…? Or rather, with whom?

CHAPTER 28

ALFIE POTTER had not been much of a speedway rider.

From three generations of mining stock in Mexborough, South Yorkshire, he had scratched about in second half races at Sheffield and appeared without much distinction in the reserve slots at the collier speedway at Wombwell.

But although he was no expert riding on dirt track surfaces, he was uniquely knowledgeable about track surfaces.

He had worked as a roadbuilder, with a particular interest in the most suitable aggregates for road foundations. He was reckoned to be the best around. During the war he had advised on the best and most efficient method of filling in bomb craters when the Luftwaffe had attempted to destroy the runways on Britain's fighter stations.

Unable to make much progress as a rider, Alfie could find regular employment advising and supervising foundation work on the network of new roads under construction in post-war Britain, particularly in the Midlands.

He still loved the thrill of speedway, paid to watch as a spectator whenever possible, and kept in touch with developments in the sport.

Alfie headed a convoy of three trucks picking up a load of foundation material at a new location, a hitherto unused quarry in Warwickshire, which specialised in a substance called shale. He had checked out its texture propensities and learned it was a finely grained and laminated sedimentary rock composed of silt and clay that parts easily along bedding planes. It was usually red-rusty in colour.

Ideal for road foundations. And when he rubbed the grains between his fingers, it clanged another bell in his memory.

He had been reading in one of the speedway publications the major stadia were actively seeking and testing new track surfaces as a workable alternative to cinders. There were sensible reasons for the search.

Ninety per cent of the major tracks, and all the flagship London stadia, shared their arena with greyhound racing. In every case, the greyhound circuit was outside the speedway so inevitably was showered with heaps of cinders during every meeting.

It was a daylong task for track staff to cover the greyhound tracks with tarpaulins, which were cumbersome and difficult to handle, particularly in any wind. But it was essential because sharp, rough edged cinders in the greyhound track did painful and sometimes career-threatening damage to the paws of the racing canine throughbreds.

Even with tarpaulins pinioned in place, flying cinders still penetrated and did damage. The greyhound operators, who ran two or three times a week and created much revenue, were not happy with the situation at all.

Also the black dust created by broadsiding back wheels left stadia with a film of filth that needed a major clean-up job.

A united appeal had been circulated for a cleaner, more manageable, less dodgy dangerous surface for speedway tracks.

Feeling the texture of a fistful of red shale, Alfie thought: "This could be the answer. It could be perfect for speedway."

By good fortune, the Warwickshire shale quarries were almost in the next parish to Coventry speedway, where their brilliant promoter Charles Appleby was perhaps the most decisive and progressive administrator in the business.

He was swift to see the potential in Alfie's proposals and volunteered to have his Brandon circuit scraped of cinders and relaid with an experimental top surface of this new red shale during the winter close season. Extensive trials were held when weather permitted. They were a marked success.

Appleby quietly bought shares in Warwickshire Quarries and arranged for the Speedway Control Board to witness his experiments, endorse his recommendations that shale be utilised for speedway racing. Straight away. As early as the 1950 season.

Critical breakthrough came when the board of the Greyhound Racing Association, who controlled most of London's tracks, unanimously agreed to lay new red shale surfaces for the new season. Their greyhound contractors were much happier with the surface.

It was the big, big speedway story at the start of a new decade, the Fifties.

In one of his most emotionally lurid leaders, Barney Stacey in the Speedway Gazette, wrote:

"A new decade, but the end of a harum-scarum age for one of the greatest collection of cavaliering crowd-pleasers the 20th century sporting entertainment business has known. Cinders have had their day. From now on around the legendary speedways of Britain, it will be red shale in the sunset. Cue tearful exit music, maestro. A generation of grimy giants of spectacle and speed who have thrilled the millions since the Roaring Twenties are leaving the the sporting stage. Like those other much-loved heroes of this century's great entertainment sensation, Chaplin, Ben Turpin, Harold Lloyd, The Keystone Cops, and the other kings of the flickering silent movies, the Cinderfellas are walking away into the sunset, into the pages of history. So long, Cinderfellas, you old beauties. Hello, Shale Shifters."

CHAPTER 29

WEST HAM upped Jacko's financial deal for the 1950 season. Even rival fans recognised appalling luck had cost him speedway's ultimate prize. He knew he was 'The People's Champion'.

With a much lighter, hopeful heart after his reunion with Fan, Jacko had headed back to Australia for the close season. He returned to the cattle station. Now it seemed natural to join Kerslake on the verandah at sundown for a beer. The old bugger seemed to enjoy his company. He went out on a two-week drove. He helped Bongo with his saddlery.

He almost forgot about speedway.

But Fan was never far from his mind.

In the New Year he had linked up with Ritchie at Claremont, Perth. Jacko politely turned down an invitation to ride at the huge Western Australian bowl. As far as riding Down Under, he felt he owed an exclusivity loyalty to the old yakker who had given him his first opportunity at Baranga way back in the Thirties. He put thousands on the crowd there on a couple of sweltering Sunday afternoons.

Ritchie seemed to have a different Sheila for every night of the week and was riproaring company. He was going like a shell around Claremont, too.

They decided to travel back to Britain together on the SS Strathavon out of Fremantle. During the wonderfully leisurely voyage Ritchie had mentioned that

Vincente Voltori had apparently agreed terms to rejoin New Cross for the 1950 season for big bucks. He'd been saying that if he could win the world championship it could lead to a Hollywood deal. Tinseltown had been signing up champions of ice skating and swimming for screen stardom. Wasn't the screen Tarzan the world backstroke champion or something?

It all restoked the fires burning inside him about Fan.

On his return to London, he left his luxurious lodging at the Dorchester. The hotel management diplomatically inferred the constant invasion by female fans required unacceptable security measures. They were also concerned many ladies who did not walk the streets for exercise were frequenting their bars in the hope of hooking such a sporting superstar.

Jacko, who always tried to be courteous to fans, was also wearying of the hysteria.

With his earnings now four times more than the Prime Minister and at Clark Gable film star level, he felt it would be improper to resume his former status as a paying guest with friends.

Besides, he was still had painful memories of the South Coast and Essex, where Vic Gordon was based.

Mulling over his gypsy lifestyle, he thought: "I seem to have spent most of my life trying to forget. Now I've got to look forward.

"It's twelve years since I first came to Britain. It's a new decade. I'm over thirty and I haven't got a home and can't imagine settling down. But it has sure been a rich and interesting life. And I still have everything to go for."

Jacko did have one place to go: Mule Terrain, where he financially underpinned the entire operation.. In fact, he'd made arrangements for all his money to be used in perpetuity for Animal Rights. There was a bedroom above the stables he could use. He had frequently used it in the past. He returned to be among his four-legged friends. He was content there.

John Shapland again grabbed the exclusive on his move.

"From the Dorchester to The Donkey Derby," he wrote. "When it comes to moving experiences, expect the unexpected from speedway's greatest contemporary star."

West Ham had arranged a daylong practice session behind closed doors to allow the Hammers to acclimatise to the new red shale track surface. Jacko spent nearly an hour trying every racing line. It was simply terrific. It suited his style perfectly. He recalled how when he had first arrived at Wimbledon as a down and out nobody he had not been permitted one single practice lap. He hadn't forgotten those days.

He collected his accumulated winter mail from the Speedway Office. There was one post-marked Paris.

It was a Bon Noel card from Fan. She had written: "Hope you have had a happy winter (or is it summer for you). Only word from Vincente is that he's returning. So am I, by the way. Court arranged a transfer to the Ministry of Defence in Whitehall. I'll be sharing a flat with Jessica in Bloomsbury. You won't believe it, I'm quite looking forward to seeing speedway again. Fan."

With a song in his heart, Jacko again immersed himself in the cheerful dressing room banter about outrageous speedway extroverts.

There was a 'Killer Bike' in the New Cross workshops which nobody could ride. Maybe they would give it to the V-Man. Ben Silva had learned to play The Harry Lime theme on his old plonker, and had struck up a relationship with lovely little Gina. Vic Gordon had swapped his Oldsmobile 88 for a Rolls Royce Silver Cloud. They were racing on frozen lakes in Sweden – the hands would never believe that back at Baranga. World champion Stan Price had been offered a full-time job in sports writing. Ralph Greenhalgh at Wimbledon had a new boy wonder from New Zealand who looked like a twelve-year-old chorister. There was a new Track Spare at Harringay called Tawdry Audrey from Lordship Lane who had a tattoo of a V2 rocket on her back disappearing up her fundament.

God, I love this life, thought Jacko.

When everyone had left the stadium, Jacko unobtrusively climbed to his special spot on the fourth bend terraces, where he always felt particularly close to Fan. He knew she had first seen speedway from that corner. It was their own Holy Ground. He wanted to be there alone

He read and re-read her card.

He felt like he was starting over: new decade, new season, new track surface, new optimism about Fan.

Renewed rivalry with Vincente Voltori.

He knew the V-Man would try to woo and win Fan. He would be flat out to win the World Championship.

But now Jacko wanted really, really wanted to win.

He wanted that world title. But most of all he wanted to win Fan back.

It was going to be quite a year.

Jacko just couldn't wait to get started.

END

237

Author's note

Cinderfellas was originally conceptualised and commissioned as a screenplay.

As the pipers who call the tune, the commissioners requested two different endings for Jacko.

Here is the alternative.

If you've paid your money and bought the book, you're entitled to choose which one you prefer!

Dave Lanning.

IN A BUDDING April of the brave new decade, West Ham were invited to a challenge match at Southampton.

With his South Coast contacts, Nipper Corbin had used his influence to get the senior club with the most glamorous box office attraction – Jacko Rintzen – to appear at the Second Division centre.

The Saints, bursting with ambition, were staging a charity night at their pretty, fairylight-festooned arena in an attempt to gain civic respectability. They even agreed to allow the Salvation Army to have a collection. During the interval, Jacko had gone into the terraces with a bucket to collect cash. He had been mobbed, taken over twenty minutes to escape.

When he delivered his weighty cache of coinage, he had been embarrassed when the head Sally Army lady had said: "Thank you sir. God will reward you."

O'Reilly's words had curiously flashed across his mind: God may well be a dog. It's the same three letters.

In the first half of the meeting, Jacko had completely outclassed the local Southampton riders, likeable, enthusiastic but from a lower level of racing. After the break, the Southampton promoter suggested to Jacko it would make racing more interesting for the capacity crowd if he started from a thirty yard handicap. He would pay him an extra pound a yard.

It was no sweat for Jacko. He had started his racing career in handicaps way back at Baranga in the Thirties.

But it was a very big deal indeed for the excited young local ex grass track star who, at the end of the first lap, found himself actually ahead of the famous Jacko Rintzen, arguably the best rider on earth.

Jacko had swept past his other two rivals and was measuring up the kid ahead. The lad was riding middle-to-outside and clearly going as fast as he possibly could.

Best to hit him hard up the inside, lock up and shift him over.

Jacko swooped. At that identical moment, his young rival's engine seized solid. It stopped within a bike length. There was no way Jacko could avoid him.

Jacko flicked his opponent's back wheel, screwing his own machine straight. Straight at the safety fence.

The fence at Southampton was not solid. It was installed inside the greyhound track. It would give on impact. It collapsed when man and machine, at full throttle impacted.

Across the greyhound circuit, the track floodlights were on solid steel stanchions at 15-yard intervals. They were strung with fairylights.

Had Jacko been thrown a foot to the right or left, he would have missed the stanchion.

But he didn't.

He did not bounce. It was not pretty. He smashed into steel with a force that snapped the stanchion, disintergrating the floodlight in a starburst shower of sparks. Yards of fairylights whipped into a shocked terrace.

Every light in the stadium went out.

Jacko Rintzen had gone to discover if God had fur and four paws.

BRITISH SPEEDWAY, in deep purple mourning, agreed it would be right and proper for John Shapland, who had a very special relationship with Jacko, to accompany his remains back to Baranga for burial.

To report, with dignity, his final journey, his last ride.

Kerslake had insisted Jacko should go home. West Ham paid for the journey. All Jacko's money was promised to Animal Rights, Mule Terrain and the Retired Greyhounds Welfare.

Jacko's greatest pals, Chinners, Nipper, Vic Gordon, Trev the Taxi, said their silent farewells at London Airport. Dribbler stood quietly in the background.

His Hammer team-mates, headed by Ritchie Mackay, carried the casket to the hold of the QANTAS aircraft. Ben Silva, tears streaming, had picked up Jacko's white silk face scarf, so lovingly embroidered by Ruthie all those years ago, in the Southampton ambulance room. He was going to give it to Gina.

Ensuring the casket was safely stowed. Shapland noticed that somehow one red rose had been attached.

There was a message: To Jacko. You will be the only one, always. Fan.

Funny, thought Shapland.
You would have thought a fan would have put a name.

END

INDEX OF PHOTOGRAPHS